AMERICAN INDIAN
LOVE STORIES

AMERICAN INDIAN
LOVE STORIES

Herman Grey

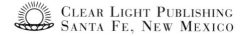

CLEAR LIGHT PUBLISHING
SANTA FE, NEW MEXICO

First Edition
10 9 8 7 6 5 4 3 2 1

Library of Congress Cataloging-in-Publication Data
Grey, Herman.
  American Indian love stories: traditional stories of love & romance
from tribes across America / by Herman Grey.— 1st ed.
      p. cm.
Summary: A collection of tales from the Hopi, Pima, Yurok, Tohono
O'Odham, Navajo, Acoma, Cochiti, Seminole and Massachusett,
which feature love and romance in the context of Native American
culture.
  ISBN 1-57416-063-x (pbk.)
  1. Indians of North America—Folklore. 2. Love—North
America—Folklore. [1. Indians of North America—Folklore. 2.
Love—Folklore. 3. Folklore—North America.] I. Title.
  E98.F6G65 2003
  398.2'089'97—DC21
                                                    2002156510

Cover painting: *Eden Two*, ©John Fadden
Edited by Sara Held
Cover design by Marcia Keegan & Carol O'Shea
Interior design & typography by Carol O'Shea
Printed in the U.S.A.

A note about the tribal names in this book:
In the last several years, several tribes have reverted to their original
names, away from the names more familiar to most of us. In accordance
with this development, we have taken the liberty of changing the tribal
names in the stories as follows:
Pima—Akimel O'Odham; Papago—Tohono O'Odham
Massachusett is not a misprint; that is how the tribal name is spelled.

CONTENTS

QUAIL
A Tohono O'Odham (Papago) Story

Deep in a large mesquite forest in the Tohono
O'Odham (Papago) Indian country was a village
called Wakimagi. Hidden by the forest from the
other villages, Wakimagi was not well-known, and
few visitors came there. Even Apache raiders never
knew of the village, because of the thickness of the
mesquite forest that surrounded it. Because it had
only one trail leading in and out, the village was
easy to defend against all raiders. With water from
a small, clear stream a short distance from the
village, the people were able to grow gardens of
corn, beans, squash and sunflowers.

Once a year in the month of September, called
Washai Gakithog Mashath (the dry-grass month),

the village celebrated a Thanksgiving ceremony to honor Elder Brother for their good harvest. Several days before the celebration, a group of men was selected to go on a trading mission to the different villages. On their backs they carried their burden baskets *(Ki-Ho')* loaded with ollas of dried corn and squash and smaller ollas filled with wild honey. Some of the men brought water ollas, which were prized by other villages. Visiting other Tohono villages as well as Yaqui and Akimel (Pima) villages to the north, they traded for cotton cloth, iron knives, beads, salt and bright-colored ribbons. One of the villages they visited was called Haiwani-wawhia.

Before they left, they invited the people of Haiwani-wawhia to come to Wakimagi to help them celebrate their Thanksgiving ceremony. They told them there would be games for the children, gambling for the grown people, kick-ball races, wrestling for the young warriors, a bow-and-arrow contest for the hunters and a long-distance race for all the men. For the young

women there would be ceremonial dances day and
night, and in the evening there would be songs
and stories for all. Of course there would be food
all day and all night.

In the village of Wakimagi, the ceremonial leader,
called the Keeper of the Smoke, was a powerful
man named Ruma (Mawith). He had a beautiful
fourteen-year-old daughter whose name was Quail
(Kakaichu). She was the leading dancer of the
village women. Quail was now of an age to marry,
and many hopeful young warriors began visiting
Ruma's dwelling, hoping to talk to Quail's parents.
Some of them even came with their own parents in
hopes of arranging a marriage between the families.

Quail refused to talk to them and chased the young
men away. She told her parents that she did not
wish to marry yet. She would not choose any of the
young warriors of their village or any other young
man she had met. None of them was the warrior
she dreamed of. Her mother told her, "If you do not
marry soon you will lose your youth, you will be

too old to marry a young warrior. When you are too old, you will only be able to marry an old man, perhaps a man already married, and you will be the second wife."

Her aunt, who was visiting, spoke up. "There is a fine young warrior here in our village," she said. "He is the best hunter. You know him, he is the one called Ravan (Hawani) of the Badger Clan. He told his parents he wanted you for his wife, and he would fight anyone else who would try to marry you. He tells the other warriors he could have any other girl he wanted for his wife but he will have you."

Quail replied, "I know Ravan, but I don't like him. I will wait for the warrior I saw in my dreams."

Her mother asked, "What did you see in your dream, an Apache, a Yaqui perhaps, or an Akimel?"

Quail replied, "Mother, I see a fine, strong warrior not of our village. I have seen him in the moon, in the stars, and once I saw him as a high-flying eagle. I don't know who he will be, but I know I will find him, and that's who I want for my husband. Even if he lives far, far away in another village, I will go with him."

"You are a pretty girl but a foolish one," her aunt said. "You live in a dream world. If you are not careful, a witch doctor will put a curse on you, and then no warrior will want you for a wife. You must choose a husband from our village. That is the custom of our people."

The village traders returned home after a week's absence, their burden baskets heavy with trade goods. They reported that the people from Haiwani-wawhia village had accepted their invitation to help with the celebration of their Thanksgiving ceremony. In a day or two four of their young warriors would arrive to help set up camps, and the rest of the people would follow soon after.

There was much to be done. The men had to hunt deer, bighorn sheep, rabbit and other game to feed

the village and their visitors during the ceremony.
The women and children were busy digging wild
onions, potatoes and other roots. The women
cooked beans, squash, cactus buds and fruit. To
make a sweet drink, they ground up mesquite pods
that had been soaked in water.

The next day the four young warriors from
Haiwani-wawhia arrived. The people welcomed
them and treated them well. Their leader was a
tall, strongly built young man who had fine facial
features and long black hair hanging to his
shoulders and tied at the end. A white eagle plume
gently waved on the top of his head.

The young maidens of the village could not stop
looking at him, and many of them smiled at him,
hoping he would smile back. When Quail looked at
him, a faint smile came over her face, and she felt
her heart skip a beat. Then he saw her, and she
quickly turned away.

One of the village men led the young warriors away
to settle in their campsite, and the young maidens

gathered to talk about them. Quail asked, "What is that tall one called?"

One of the girls replied, "I heard my father tell my mother the names of all four of them." She looked at Quail and said, "The one you asked about, he is called Eagle (Ba'-agi). He is good-looking, but me, I don't care for him. The one I like is called Roadrunner (Todai). I think he is much better. Quail, I think you like Eagle, I saw you smile at him."

Quail's face changed color as she quickly replied, "I didn't say I liked him, I just asked what he was called!"

"Perhaps Eagle is the dream you have been waiting for," another maiden said. "Now what will Ravan say when he learns that you like Eagle?"

Quail angrily replied, "I don't care what Ravan may say, he will not be my husband, I don't like Ravan."

The next morning Quail went to the stream to fetch water for her mother, carrying an olla on her head.

She placed the olla on the ground and began pouring water into it from her gourd dipper. She felt like something or someone or even a spirit were watching her. She laid her dipper down. She slowly turned and looked all around, but she didn't see anyone. She was worried now because she noticed it was too quiet in the forest.

She didn't know that Ravan had gone ahead of her and was hiding behind a large tree nearby.

Quail was uneasy. She couldn't decide what to do. Should she run on home and try to explain to her parents why she had come home without any water and have people laugh at her foolishness? Or take what water she had and hurry home, telling her parents that she felt some danger in the forest? Then she thought perhaps it was Eagle who was nearby to protect her and she would be running away from him. She knew she loved him, she felt it in her heart, but if it were Eagle, why didn't he come out from hiding? Didn't he want to speak to her?

She decided to wait, hoping it was Eagle. As she poured water into the olla slowly and carefully, she was thinking of him. Suddenly her heart began to beat faster—she heard footsteps coming up behind her. She wanted to whirl around, but her knees stiffened. A sudden ripple ran up and down her back as she felt a hand clamp down on her shoulder. She said to herself, "Oh, spirit of the rainbow, let it be Eagle!"

Her hope was broken when she heard a voice she knew say, "Are you waiting for Eagle?"

It was Ravan—the last person she wanted to see. Her heart felt as if it were torn out of her body, but she pulled herself together quickly. She shook off his hand and turned around to face him. "No, I was not waiting for anyone," she replied, "but now I wish it were Eagle instead of you, so go away and leave me alone."

"You cannot become Eagle's wife," Ravan told her angrily. "He is of another village. And I will beat him in the bow-and-arrow contest, I will throw him in the wrestling and I will beat him in the long race. You know that the one who wins in the long run gets to choose any girl he wants for his wife, and I know I will win."

Then he left and went to look up the earthquake doctor, who was his uncle.

When the young warriors first arrived in the village, Eagle saw Quail, and he thought she was the most beautiful maiden he had ever seen in his life. But he thought she was already spoken for, and he wasn't there to make trouble.

The next morning, Eagle went to the stream to wash his body. As he made his way there, he was thinking of Quail. Before he reached the water, he heard someone hurrying along the trail back to the village. Eagle quickly slipped behind some trees and waited. As the person came hurrying by, Eagle peeked out and saw that it was Ravan. He was mumbling to himself and seemed angry.

Eagle waited till Ravan was out of sight. He went on to the stream, and to his surprise he saw Quail pouring water into the olla.

Again Quail felt someone was watching her. "Oh, no—what does Ravan want now," she thought. "Why doesn't he go on home and leave me alone?"

She straightened up and turned around. When she saw Eagle, her legs got so weak she almost fell over. She calmed herself down, but her heart was pounding. At last her dream had come for her. There he stood smiling, and she smiled back at him. They laughed together, all at once in their own world. Her heart told her he was the one for her, and he too had the feeling he had found the one he would always love.

She asked him, "How long have you been watching me?"

"I just came here to wash myself," Eagle replied. "I didn't know you were here. On my way I saw Ravan hurrying back, he looked very angry. Is he the one who has spoken for you?"

Quail's heart was still pounding, but she did not want to seem too eager. She looked at him without smiling. "How long have you been watching me?" she asked again.

Eagle felt hurt by her coldness and replied, "I told you it wasn't long, I just got here and saw you. You are very pretty."

Quail asked, "What do you want?"

Eagle didn't answer right away. Then he said, "I will not bother you anymore." He turned away and walked off.

Quail didn't understand. What had she done? She wanted to run after him and explain how she felt and tell him she was not angry with him, but it was too late. Her thoughts went back to his question, "Is he the one who has spoken for you?" She called out, "I don't want him, and no one has spoken for me!" But only the breeze heard her.

Tears filled her eyes, her heart hurt, her stomach was burning. She was sure she had lost her dream, the warrior she dreamed she would marry.

Picking up her olla, Quail placed it on her head and went home with tears rolling down her cheeks.

When she arrived home, she carefully put the olla down and ran to her mother. "Mama, I just made a fool of myself," she said. "I met the man I dreamed of, the one I have been waiting for, and like a fool I chased him away. Mama, what is wrong with me, why did I do that? I also met Ravan and we had words. Do you think the earthquake doctor put a curse on me? I know we are not too friendly with him."

Her mother replied, "I don't believe there is a curse on you, it's just part of growing up. When we are young, sometimes we do foolish things. We hurt ourselves, then we feel sorry. Whichever way you make your life, time will cover it. I'm sure you will see him again."

The next day the people from Haiwani-wawhia arrived. That afternoon the ceremony got under way. The women started it with games of *to-ka*. Later the men played the kicking ball games. Each village had two teams, and the goals were one mile apart. Others played the bamboo gambling game.

Late that afternoon before sunset the young maidens began the Sun Dance. The maidens formed a large circle and danced around it with a swaying clockwise movement. In the center of the circle stood a young man who represented the sun. The dancers extended their hands toward him as they sang the song, "The dwelling place of the sun, the giver of life."

Quail was the lead dancer. She held her head high and proud, but her eyes searched everywhere for Eagle. She didn't see him. She felt disappointed and wished she could leave the dance and go on home.

From the back of the crowd Eagle watched the maidens dance and kept his eyes on Quail, hoping she could see him. He wanted to talk to her once more and ask her if she were spoken for. If she were, he would go home. He would not wrestle or take part in the bow-and-arrow contest or even run in the long run—he would go home that very night. He wanted her, and he wanted to win her, but if she were spoken for, it would just hurt him more to stay there and see her every day and not be able to claim her.

He moved away from the crowd and walked into the darkness, where he found a large rock. He sat down. From there he could see the ceremonial fires and the dancers in the distance, and he could think. He was so deep in thought that he did not feel anyone come up behind him till two cool, soft hands clamped over his eyes.

Startled, he reached back and grabbed the person's arms. He knew right away that they were a woman's. When he heard a gentle laugh, his heart skipped several beats. He said, "Quail, it's you."

She came around to face him and answered, "Yes, it's me. I looked for you during the dancing, but I didn't see you anywhere. When I saw you leave, I

15

decided to look for you. Why did you come here, why did you leave the ceremony?"

Eagle held her hands in his and replied, "Quail, I watched you dance every step, and my heart went out with pride for you, but I know I have no chance as you are already spoken for."

Quail's eyes blazed like fire as she answered, "I have not been spoken for, it is you I dream of, it is you I have been waiting for, can't you see?"

Eagle squeezed her hands and asked, "What about Ravan? Will his uncle make war on our village?"

Quail replied, "No, I am old enough to marry the one I choose. After the ceremonies, come to my dwelling and talk to my parents and ask for me. They will understand."

That morning, Ravan had gone home feeling very angry at Quail for refusing him, and he was worried that Eagle would try to win her. He went to his Uncle Earthquake's dwelling, hoping to get revenge. He told his uncle that people were making fun of him, the girls turned their backs to him, and he needed help.

His uncle said he would help him. "I know how far the race will be this year," he told Ravan. "The race is to the salty waters. Each runner must bring back a bag of salt, which will be used for medicine power. It will be a two-day race, because the salty waters are far away. I will use my earthquake power to make the rattlesnakes come out in Eagle's path. They will bite him, and he will die. The bag of salt is the proof that the runner did run to the salty waters. But you must do your part, you are to run very fast, get in front of everyone till you come to a big hill. Behind the hill is a cave, and I will hide a bag of salt there. You have to stay there till the following day. In the late afternoon, you run back here and you will be the winner."

On the second day the contests began. Eagle and Ravan did better than the other warriors. In the bow-and-arrow contest, Eagle and Ravan shot matching scores. In the wrestling matches, Ravan and Eagle were matched against each other, and each of them won two falls. The final test, the long run, would be held early the next morning.

Before the start, the ceremonial officer, the Keeper of the Smoke, went up to the runners to give them their last instruction: They were to bring back from the salty waters a bag of salt and a seashell. Ravan heard what the Keeper of the Smoke said, and he figured the earthquake doctor would put the shell in the bag of salt.

Early the next morning, before the giver of life sent out his rays on earth mother, the long race began. Ravan quickly ran on ahead. After a long run he came to the hill, where he found the cave and inside it, a bag of salt. He hid himself and waited. It wasn't too long before the other runners came by, with Eagle in the lead. It would take the rest of the day and even part of the night for all of them to reach the salty waters. There they would bathe in the water, fill their bags with salt, find a seashell and return home.

Late in the afternoon of the next day, Ravan came out of his hiding place and started running back to the village. The Keeper of the Smoke had stationed young scouts along the trail about two miles apart to escort the front runner.

Ravan ran for some time before the first scout saw him. Waiting till Ravan came alongside, the scout joined him. They ran till they picked up all the other scouts along the way, except for one who stayed behind. The scouts escorted Ravan to the center of the village, where they were greeted by the crowd with wild shouts and yells.

Quail's mother had been watching her daughter and saw her go back to their dwelling. Her mother was worried. She knew Quail would need her now. She found her sitting on a log, her favorite place. She was crying.

In the center of the village, Ravan was holding his bag of salt high overhead. He called out, "I am the best runner, and I claim Quail."

The Keeper of the Smoke asked Ravan, "The bag of salt that you hold, did you get it at the salty waters?"

Ravan replied, "Yes."

The Keeper of the Smoke asked a second question. "Where is the seashell you were told to bring with the salt?"

Ravan looked inside the bag of salt. There was no seashell. He changed from joyful boasting to wild anger as the people also asked, "Yes, Ravan, where is the seashell?"

Yelling back at them, he pushed his way through the crowd and rushed away from the village. He disappeared into the hills and was never seen in his village again.

Just before the sun set, the scout who had stayed behind ran into the village center and called out, "Eagle is coming in, and the other runners are not too far behind."

As Quail and her mother talked, they heard shouting and yelling again. Her mother said, "I am sure that is your dream, it has to be Eagle. He is a real warrior. Ravan must have played some trick with his Uncle Earthquake."

Quail's hopes brightened, her heart grew bigger, and she could hardly breathe for excitement. Her eyes were clear now and sparkling.

Quail's happy face made her mother smile. "Come on, daughter," she said laughing, "let's go see the winning warrior before some other girl gets him."

Quail replied, "No, mother, he is my dream, he loves me. He will come and ask you and father for me, and then I will go with him to his village."

THE CROW MOTHER KACHINA MAIDEN

A Hopi Love Story

Many years ago, in one of the Hopi villages, there
lived a beautiful young maiden who was of
marriageable age but had not bothered to choose or
accept any of the young men of her village—or
even the other villages—for her husband. She was a
good and kind person, and everyone loved her.
Called Purple Flower ("Tolakya"), the name given
her when she was initiated into the Kachina society
at the age of ten, she belonged to her mother's clan,
the Parrot Clan, one of the early clans of the
village of Oraibi.

Many young men from the other villages made
special trips to see her and try to win her over.
Even some Tasavuh (Navajo), Zunis and others

from as far as Isleta Pueblo on the Rio Grande
came, but Purple Flower turned them all down. Her
mother would ask, "What are you waiting for?"
and Purple Flower would answer, "I don't know,
perhaps one day someone will come here, someone I
see in my dreams. I don't know where he is from or
what clan he belongs to, but there is someone
somewhere that I will want." Her mother asked
again, "How will you know this young man?"
Purple Flower replied, "Perhaps Crow Mother
Kachina will help if I believe in the teachings of
our elders."

Some days later, Purple Flower was chosen by the
Pawami Chief to be the Crow Mother Kachina for
the Bean Dance. The day before the dance, Purple
Flower appeared as the Crow Mother Kachina at the
Po'ki' (dog) shrine, which was close to the village.
There she began singing in her beautiful voice.

Purple Flower looked lovelier than ever. She wore
two large crow wings with tufted feathers on each
side of her blue mask. On her face were painted

two inverted black triangles. Her black dress was secured at her waist with a long, fringed white wedding belt. Over her shoulder she wore a beautiful embroidered bride's blanket. Her feet were clothed in knee-length white bridal buckskin moccasins. Finally, her neck was graced with a ruff of spruce boughs.

When she finished her song, she moved to the edge of the village and sang another song, one describing her people and clan's migration. This song took some time to sing, for it told of many places.

By the time she came to the end of the song, she was tired. With a deep sigh, she sang the last notes, ending her journey. The chief came to her and took the plaque she had been carrying, then gave her a blessing with a prayer feather. She started for her house.

She turned a corner near a house, thinking about her performance and not paying attention to where she was going. Suddenly, she bumped into a young man and was knocked back a few steps. As she regained her balance, she stared with blazing eyes at him and said angrily, "Why don't you look where you're going? You want all the ground?"

The boy was startled, and in a clumsy way he tried to make room for Purple Flower to pass. She wanted to stay angry but she couldn't. Smiling to herself, she said more softly, "Will you please move? I want to go home."

The young man stepped farther away—his mouth still open and his heart beating fast. This was the prettiest girl he had ever seen. He followed her with his eyes until she disappeared behind a house. Purple Flower then backed up and peeked around the corner, seeing the young man still standing there. She smiled to herself then turned around and went on home.

All the way home, she thought about him. She couldn't get him out of her mind. As she pictured him, she felt a tingle in her body. She thought to herself, "He must be the one I've been waiting for!"

When she reached her home, she told her mother about the young man and how she felt. Her mother smiled as she asked, "Who is he? Where is he from, and what Clan is he from?" Purple Flower seemed not to hear her. She kept the young man in her thoughts, and she too wondered who he was and where he was from. She had never seen him before, but he seemed to know his way around the village, and he wasn't one of those who had come to court her.

Purple Flower changed her clothes and told her mother she was going to see the rest of the dance. Circling the village, she carefully looked for him while keeping out of sight as much as possible. She couldn't find him.

Finally she asked one of the women baking bread in her outside oven if she had seen a young stranger. The woman looked at her and smiled before she replied, "Why, did you lose one?" Then she laughed and said, "Yes, I have seen many strangers," and turned back to her work.

Purple Flower was disappointed and decided to go
back home, when suddenly she felt as if someone
were watching her. She quickly turned around, but
she didn't see him. Again she was disappointed and
hurt, then she thought to herself, "Why should I
care when there are other young men I can choose
from? Why should I care?"

She continued on, but soon she heard footsteps
coming up behind her. Her heart skipped a beat,
and she slowed down, then quickly turned around.
Again it wasn't him; it was a Zuni man who soon
passed her. Her heart grew heavy, and she was
almost angry as she said to herself, "Oh, I don't
care if I never see him again. There are others."

Suddenly, to her surprise, she saw him, at the
edge of the mesa near where she had sung earlier
that morning. Her heart started beating fast.
He was looking at her. She felt confused. What
should she do? What should she say? If she sent
him away, wouldn't she be miserable for the rest
of her life?

Without knowing what she would say, she slowly walked up to him. He looked at her for what seemed a very long time before he spoke. Then in a clear fine voice he said, "You are Purple Flower. Many people know of you. You are of the Parrot Clan. I am Sunstops of the Water Clan. We are a small, poor clan. Our men belong to the warrior society, so I don't have much to offer your family. That is why I did not come to try to win your love."

Purple Flower could now breathe easier, so she replied, "That does not matter. You are the one I have been waiting for. My family will help us."

Sunstops shook his head as he said, "No, I will take help from no one. I am a warrior. You are like the stars at night, bright and beautiful and far above me. I would like nothing better than to marry you, but I cannot have you; I have nothing to offer you."

Purple Flower's eyes were clouded with tears, as she softly replied, "You have yourself to offer me. If you are poor, then I am poor. We have found

each other; you are the one I want. We have good
feelings for each other, which make both of us
happy and filled with joy."

Sunstops smiled and said, "I can see now that you
are the one I dreamed of one night. I saw you in
that dream, just as I see you now." Then his face
grew serious as he continued, "But even so, even
though I have found you, I must leave you, for I
am a warrior. As you know, there is trouble with
the Tasavuh raiding our villages. I don't know
what will happen.

"I must tell you," he continued, "you have never
seen me here before, but I am from here. It's only
that I am gone most of the time. You see, as a young
boy, I always wanted to be a warrior, but my father
said I had to wait until I had reached my
seventeenth circle of plantings. It was then that I
had my first experience in battle with the Tasavuh."

One day when they came to raid one of the villages,
I was scared, but I shot all my arrows at the
Tasavuh. I wanted to be a brave warrior. Our war

chief then told me that if I wanted to be a warrior, I had to make the journey to Keresan land and seek the Muskrat House and take with me many sacrifices. I had to go there in the middle of the night. I was to go to a village called Cocohiti. There, one of their warriors would guide me to the Muskrat House, and he would then tell me what I was to do next.

"I went to Cocohiti and found the warrior who guided me to the Muskrat House. There I took off my clothing and sprinkled sacred corn meal on the ground near a pool of water. Then I went into the water and sat down, so that the water covered my body up to my neck. While I was in the water, I felt as if someone or a spirit were pulling at me. After what seemed a long struggle, I climbed out, put on my clothes and started back home. I was told not to look back at the house or to run; I was to walk slowly.

"As I walked, once more, I felt as if I someone or a spirit were pulling on me, trying to make me look backwards. I had been told that if I panicked and looked back or ran, I would either get killed or never become a brave warrior. I didn't panic or look back, and I have never been afraid since. Now I have to go when I am called, whenever there is trouble."

Purple Flower reached for Sunstops' hand and held it close to her cheek, then she said, "I understand. I know you have to go. I don't want you to, but I know you must, and I will be here. I will wait for you. You must come back. It's not fair—we have just met. But we will be together when you come back."

Early the next morning a runner from another village came to Purple Flower's village. He was seeking the leaders to tell them that his village needed help; it was under attack from the Tasavuh raiders. The war chief asked the young warriors of their village if they would go, and many did. Sunstops was one of them. They all prepared themselves for war and soon were on their way.

Purple Flower didn't see Sunstops leave, but she
felt he was gone. She could see him in her thoughts
after he left, so she went out to look for him, to be
sure he had gone, and she did not find him
anywhere. From that day on she changed. She ate
very little and hardly slept. Every day she would go
to the edge of the mesa and wait for him.

One day, her mother came to her at her usual place
and sat down beside her and said, "Purple Flower,
do not waste your life waiting. There are many
things you can do to help me. Come on home."
Purple Flower agreed with her mother and thought
it would be better for her to stay busy. That might
also make the time go faster.

Some days later Purple Flower's father told her
that he had been approached by a friend of his
from the Bear Clan who had a son who wanted to
marry her. He had agreed and was now preparing
for the wedding to take place a week after the time
of the Bean Dance. Purple Flower replied that she
did not want to marry anyone else, only Sunstops.

Her father told her that the young man he had chosen came from a great and famous clan, and he pointed out that Sunstops could be dead by now, because the battle he was fighting in was very fierce. Also, here was her chance to help her clan by marrying well.

Stubbornly, Purple Flower said she would still wait for Sunstops. Her father became angry and replied, "You have been chosen to be a wife. You cannot go against my wishes." Purple Flower replied she would run off into the desert before she would marry anyone but Sunstops.

Early the next morning, a runner came to the village to announce that the battle was over. The Tasavuh had been driven away, and the warriors were on their way back. The next day, the warriors did come back, bringing with them their wounded and dead. Word spread quickly throughout the village of their return. Families came out looking for their warriors, their wounded and their dead.

Purple Flower came out looking for Sunstops, but she couldn't find him. She asked one of the war captains about him. He told her that he saw Sunstops go down fighting with four Tasavuh and was sure he was killed, because the Tasavuh always smash their enemies' heads. Sunstops was never found, so the captain thought the Tasavuh had carried him away.

Purple Flower was stunned. Her heart stopped, she couldn't catch her breath and she almost fell, but her mother caught her in her arms. She tried to cry, but she couldn't. Her mind was in a whirl.

Only when she was taken home did she fully realize what had apparently happened. She still couldn't believe it; she didn't want to believe it. "It's not true, it's not true," she kept telling herself. For the next three days, she wandered around in a daze, and when her father asked her if she were ready to marry the boy he had chosen, she said she didn't care whom she married.

The wedding was set for a week after the Bean
Dance, and by chance she was chosen once more
to be the Crow Mother Kachina. Still, she would
go to the edge of the mesa early each morning
and gaze towards the direction where Sunstops
was last seen.

On the morning of the dance, she went out to sing
the songs of the migration. As she finished and
waited for the chief, she heard footsteps behind
her, and she sadly and slowly turned around. Then
her heart stopped. She could not believe her eyes;
her body was shaking all over—for there in front of
her stood Sunstops. They stared at each other
before Sunstops said, "Purple Flower, I am back. I
was captured, but I managed to escape, and I've
come back to you."

Purple Flower breathed a long sigh as tears filled
her eyes, and she said, "I am so glad, so happy, I
almost gave up. They told me you had been fighting
four Tasavuh, and they could not find you
afterwards, so they thought that you were killed

and your body taken away, but here you are back. Somehow I knew you would come back to me."

Purple Flower and Sunstops went to her mother's house and declared that she would marry him instead of the other man, even if they would be forced to move from the village. Sunstops had proven himself to be a brave warrior, and they would be welcomed in other villages. However, after a lengthy discussion, the village elders finally consented to the marriage between Purple Flower and Sunstops, and their wedding was held on the previously chosen day, a week after the Bean Dance.

YELLOW FEATHER
An Acoma Love Story

In the village of Acoma, home of the people of the
White Rock Mesa, there once lived a beautiful
maiden of seventeen years who was still not
married. In those early years, a maiden of
seventeen was thought to be past the age of
marriage. Her family wanted her to marry a young
warrior of the Eagle (Tyami) Clan, which was not
related to her clan, the Parrot (Shawiti) Clan. If
she did not choose to marry anyone of their village,
they were in hopes she would choose a Zuni
warrior. These two tribes had always had a strong
bond, having migrated together from the villages of
Topitsiama and Katzima in the Enchanted Mesa
after leaving Shipapu, their place of beginning.

The young maiden was given the name "Yellow Feather" because, on the morning of her birth, a small whirlwind racing through the village had left behind a single yellow parrot feather at the doorway of their dwelling. This was considered a good omen for the village.

At the age of fourteen she had many suitors from other villages, even as far off as Isleta and Laguna. But she turned them all down. The village people would shake their heads and whisper that she had been bewitched by a powerful lightning doctor, who had wanted her for his son, whom she had turned down. They believed she would never marry until that spell was broken by someone not of their tribe or their people.

At first Yellow Feather did not mind being unmarried, but after seeing girls her age and younger lovingly caring for their children, she began to feel left out and lonely. She tried to keep herself as busy as she could, making pottery and taking care of her family's flock of turkeys.

But her work was not enough to make her happy. Each evening she would go down the rough trail her people had cut in the rock, and halfway down the mesa at the turkey pens, she would stop at a place she had chosen for herself. There she would sing to the moon and stars, asking them to find and bring to her a brave warrior who would love and marry her. Sometimes she became so depressed with loneliness that she cried and called out to the fireflies to light the way for her dream warrior to come for her.

One day there was great excitement in the village when a person not of her people appeared at the foot of the mesa and called up to the people. Two warriors were hastily sent down the trail to escort this white stranger up to the village. The white stranger, who was dressed in long, dusty brown cloth, pointed to himself and said, "I am Fray Marcos de Niza." In his other hand he held a shiny metal stick with a shiny bar of metal fastened across it. The white person did not stay long. After he had drunk water and eaten, he went away to the west.

Some days later a band of thirty strangely dressed white men came part way up the trail toward the village, carrying long black sticks that thundered and made smoke. The people had seen these attackers coming, and the village warriors fought them. Their leader, whose name was Captain Juan de Zalivar, was killed, as were two other leaders who carried long knives hanging from their belts. Fourteen of the other soldiers were also killed in the battle. The rest of them ran away down the trail, except for four who jumped from the mesa to the ground—as far below as the height of a very tall tree.

Three of the soldiers who jumped were not hurt badly, but the fourth one just lay on the ground without moving. The other three ran off, not bothering to help him. This badly hurt young man was a soldier of the queen of Spain. His name was Fernando de Sanchez. His uncle, Don de Sanchez, was Queen Isabella's treasurer. Young Fernando had been sent out to the New World to go with Captain Juan de Zalivar to find new lands to add to the family's estate. The design of the De Sanchez crest was a gold-and-green beetle found only in Africa.

Young Fernando had injured his left shoulder, and he had a badly sprained left ankle and a bad wound on his left temple. The fall knocked him out, and he lay where he had fallen for some time.

When he finally came to, he realized what had happened and he feared for his life. He was sure the village warriors would come down to check on the soldiers who had jumped off the mesa, to see if they were all dead. In great pain, young Fernando began to crawl away around the bottom of the cliff, looking for a place to hide. Moving made the pain worse, but he could not stop and rest. The urge to live kept him going, and he knew enough to cover the trail he was making by throwing sand and dirt over it.

Finally he found a cleft in the cliff wall. He crawled in as far as he could and lay down. He tried to cover himself up with whatever he could find there—rocks, sand, old bones, and dried pieces of brush. His pain was so great that he couldn't help but moan every time he moved. After he covered himself, he lay still and tried to get some rest.

His heart almost stopped as he heard human voices some distance away. He was sure that village warriors were nearby searching for tracks and signs, for they would know now that the soldiers were not killed and were out there somewhere trying to escape. One of the warriors knew of the cleft and was about to search inside it when the shout of the warrior leader called for everyone to gather where one of their scouts had found footprints not made by moccasins. From there they took up the chase into the desert.

When it became quiet again, Fernando fell asleep.

Some time later he was awakened by the sound of voices. He did not remember where he was or what had happened and only knew that he was in terrible pain. He tried to call out, but he could only groan softly, not loud enough to be heard. As the voices moved off, his head cleared a little. He heard a voice chanting a song in a strange language. He tried to sit up, but he was too weak and still in great pain. Finally he gathered enough strength to push himself up, but his head was whirling around and around, and he fell back, moaning with pain.

Yellow Feather, who was walking nearby singing to herself, was surprised to hear moaning. She stopped in her tracks to listen. At first she thought it was the wind, but she could feel no wind on her hair or skin. The groaning started again. She looked around, following the sound, and soon discovered the cleft. She was surprised for she had not known it was there. The moaning began again, and she knew it came from inside.

Her heart began to beat a little faster. She felt scared and wondered what she should do. Should she run back up to the village and tell her people?

If they came down and found nothing in the cleft, they would say she was still bewitched, hearing and seeing things. She decided to look inside the cleft herself and see who or what was inside.

She took a deep breath and slowly and carefully made her way into the cleft. It was narrow and partly dark inside, but her eyes got used to the darkness, and she could just make out the sand floors and steep walls. A loud groan startled her, and she jumped back. She didn't know what was in there, but she hoped the groaning was coming from a human.

Moving in a little farther, she saw the mound of sand, sticks, bones and leaves. Her heart beat faster when the mound moved. Then she saw the head and face of one of the white soldiers. His eyes were closed, and his head moved a little from side to side as he moaned. She could see that he was hurt and in pain and perhaps sick as well. She studied him. He was young and good-looking. He had a black beard, and his black hair was matted with sand, sticks and small twigs. She was sure he was one of the four soldiers who had jumped off the mesa.

She thought, "What am I to do now? He is our enemy." Yet, as she looked at him, she felt sorry for him. Her heart felt heavy. It was true he was the enemy, and perhaps many more like him would come, make war with her people, and fight against her own father and brother. Yet she could see he was hurt. His dark eyes were open now, but they did not seem to focus. Perhaps he was burning with fever and would die soon, and no one would know but her. What if his spirit put a curse on their village to make their fields of corn dry up?—they would have no food to put in their storage rooms for the cold days to come. Perhaps his spirit would not put a curse on them if she helped him.

She decided to give the hurt soldier a drink of water before he died. She helped him sit up a little by putting her arm under his shoulder, and then she put her water gourd to his lips. He mumbled something she didn't understand.

Fernando's lips were parched, and he needed water. She poured a few drops into his mouth. It was cool and it was sweet, and he began to drink in big gulps, till he could feel his whole body relax.

When he stopped drinking, she gently laid his shoulders back on the ground and sprinkled a few drops on his face. She watched him drift into a deep sleep with a slight smile on his face.

She looked at him closely. Her heart seemed to warm up, and she forgot where she was. She forgot that the young man was an enemy of her people.

Yellow Feather suddenly realized it was late. She stood up, quickly made her way out of the cleft, and hurried on up the mesa to her village. All the way up she kept thinking of the soldier. She couldn't believe she was in love with him, it wasn't possible. She was just being kind to him so that he would not put a curse on their village. Everyone knew it was wrong to love an enemy of her people, but in her heart she didn't feel it was wrong. She thought to herself, "Why is it right for me to love someone but wrong for me to love someone not of my people?"

The third day after the battle, Yellow Feather asked her mother, "Who were those strange white warriors? Where did they come from, what do they want?"

Her mother replied, "I don't know where they came from, I don't know who they are. But our leaders and medicine men have been in council ever since the battle. They have sent runners to the other villages to find out more about these strangers."

Yellow Feather then asked, "What will happen if our warriors capture any of these strangers."

Her mother replied, "They will be put to death."

Yellow Feather kept on, "Why can't we make a slave of one of them if he is captured?"

"You have been acting strange ever since the white warriors came here," her mother said. "Do they bother you in your dreams?"

Yellow Feather replied, "No, but what if one of them were found, would he be put to death?"

Her mother replied, "I don't think our warriors would bring any of them into our village alive, and it is not up to us women to say what to do in such matters."

"But what if one of them should come in peace to our village," Yellow Feather said, "would we not accept him?"

Her mother laughed and replied, "Such crazy talk, you have been dreaming again. Come on and help me, it's our turn to feed the council. No more foolish talk."

Yellow Feather remembered that when the sick soldier was in deep sleep, she had seen around his neck a bright-yellow metal chain and hanging from it a beautiful green stone in the shape of a scarab, a winged beetle. She had noticed that on its flat underside was engraved a symbol of a bird, which she figured must be his clan. She had never seen the yellow metal or a bright-green stone like that before, and she was confused by the strangeness of these things. Yet the thought of him sent ripples through her body.

She wanted to tell her mother her secret, but would her mother understand? What would the village leaders say or do to her? She was sure they would kill the young soldier. The very thought of that frightened her so much that her stomach felt sick. She thought, "I will help him get well, and then we will both escape. We will have to go far away, beyond Laguna and Isleta." Her heart felt different now—it didn't beat like it used to before she found her young soldier. Now all she wanted was to be with him.

The next day Yellow Feather told her mother she was going down to the cornfields, where their family had their plot of land. She packed some food and water and went out. She stopped by the turkey pens, where she had hidden some more food. She went out, not realizing that White Raven, the son of the lightning doctor, had been watching and following her.

When she came to the cleft, she stopped and looked around. She didn't see anyone else close by, so she slipped inside. She made her way in carefully. She came to where she had left Fernando, and to her surprise, she found him sitting up. On seeing her, he smiled weakly but with happiness. Her heart stopped, and she felt weak all over. She could see he was much improved.

He called to her softly in Spanish, "You are very pretty." She didn't understand, but she felt the love in his words. She gave him some water and food and watched as he ate ravenously. Finally he stopped eating. After wiping his mouth on his sleeve, he asked in Spanish, "What is your name?" He waited for her to answer, but she could only smile and shake her head and shrug her shoulders. Then he pointed to himself and said, "I am Fernando, Fernando de Sanchez. Who are you?"

Finally she hesitantly repeated, "Fernando," and smiled at him.

He smiled also but shook his head. He patted his chest and said, "*Me* Fernando."

Finally she understood that was his name, so she patted herself and said, "*Me* Yellow Feather."

Fernando tried to repeat her Indian name, but he couldn't, so he pointed to her and said, "You Maria. Maria pretty."

Yellow Feather replied, "*Nyumacanyisoma ke me sowcima* (I am going to help you because I like you)."

They traded words and signs back and forth, and soon they began to understand each other.

Yellow Feather saw that he was tired, so she motioned to him that she must leave.

She came back the next day and went into the cleft, but she did not see Fernando. Her heart stopped, her knees were weak. What had happened? Where did he go? Had the warriors found him, and was he now a prisoner or even dead? Perhaps he was trying to escape by himself—if he had gone out, someone was sure to find him.

She was about to go out to look for him when she suddenly felt a strong arm encircle her shoulder from behind. As she opened her mouth to yell, she heard Fernando's voice saying softly, "Maria." She had not seen him hiding deep in the cleft. She turned to face him, and her heart was beating fast. She did not know whether to scold him or cry. He tried to kiss her, but she did not understand. His lips felt warm. She had never been kissed.

Kissing was not known among her people. Love was expressed in other ways. The love between the men and women in her village was the sincere feeling of the trust one felt for the other, the bond

of love of everyday life. This was a love that
would last a lifetime on earth mother and in the
spirit world.

Finally she said, "I must go but I will be back."

White Raven saw Yellow Feather go into the cleft.
He wondered what she could be doing there. He
had been inside many times, and there was nothing
in there but trash. He was about to follow her in
when he saw her coming out.

He was well hidden, so he waited. After she was out
of sight, he carefully sneaked into the cleft. He was
very careful, for he felt he was not alone.

After a little while he saw Fernando, and he knew
he was one of the enemy soldiers who had come to
their village to make war on them.

Fernando didn't realize that someone had come into
the cleft or that he had been discovered.

White Raven silently crawled out and went on
home. His mind was whirling, and he was deep in

thought. He thought of telling his father, but he also thought of taking his revenge on Yellow Feather.

When he came to Yellow Feather's home, he called for her to come out. She was surprised, but she went out. She asked White Raven what he wanted. White Raven gave her a big smile and replied, "I learned your secret. I saw the white soldier you have been hiding in the cleft."

Yellow Feather's heart skipped a beat, and the blood in her head began to pound. She asked, "What will you do, tell the village leaders?"

White Raven laughed and replied, "I am not sure what I will do. I can tell my father, who will tell the other leaders, and he will be killed. Or I can forget what I know if you will marry me."

Yellow Feather's heart seemed to die away inside of her, and she wished for death. Then she thought, at least she could save Fernando's life. There was no other choice. So she replied, "If you promise me and really keep your promise, I will marry you. You must promise you will let him escape."

White Raven answered, "I will keep my promise. Now I will ask my father to talk to your father, and they can set the wedding date." And Raven went on home.

Yellow Feather could hardly breathe. Her body felt drained, her head ached, and she mumbled to herself, "What have I done, what did I say, what will happen now?"

Finally she regained her strength and went back inside her home.

Yellow Feather's mother soon noticed that she was not her usual self. She seemed in a daze and hardly ate. She forgot to go to the turkey pens. She only helped her mother when she asked, and her mother had to repeat everything she said to her. Her mother thought Yellow Feather must be excited about her coming wedding.

White Raven's family was happy, for Yellow Feather
was a beautiful girl and she would make their son a
good wife. There was much to do to prepare for the
wedding, lots of food to be cooked and prepared by
both families.

The village fields were about two miles away
from the mesa. The young seeds of corn, beans,
squash and tobacco had been warmed just right
by the life-giving sun. The rains and snows had
been good, and now the seeds were sprouting. It
was time for the people to go down and hoe the
weeds and set traps for the rabbits and ground
squirrels that would get into the fields and eat the
young plants.

Three nights before the wedding, Yellow Feather
heard White Raven boasting that he knew where
one of the white enemy soldiers was hiding.
He was still alive and only White Raven knew
where he was. After the wedding he would tell
where this enemy was and he would be captured
and killed.

Yellow Feather went to bed and cried. She felt
her whole world had fallen apart and her life was
over. She would never see her love again. She
thought to herself, if he is caught he will be
killed. Then she too would die, she would leap
from the mesa to her death. She had nothing
more to live for now. She would never marry
White Raven.

When everyone was asleep, she walked to the edge
of the mesa. She looked all around. It was quiet
and no one else was there. As she was about to
jump, she found she couldn't move. She tried to
break free from this unknown power that was
holding her back.

She cried and struggled within herself. Then from
the darkness she heard her mother's voice calling to
her, and suddenly she was free. She felt so weak
that she almost fell down. She turned away from
the edge of the cliff and went back to her house.
She went in and called her mother, but she found
her mother asleep.

Her head felt empty, and she began to tremble. She thought to herself, "Am I in the spirit world now? Have I left my father and mother? If I am dead and if Fernando is killed, can he go to the spirit world with me, or do his people belong to a different spirit world and he cannot be with me?" Finally her head stopped whirling, and she fell onto her bed and went to sleep.

Early the next morning her mother woke her up and said, "Yellow Feather, you must hurry and eat now because you must go to the fields before anyone else and bring back your four plants of corn for the wedding. Be sure to take your blanket. You must not talk to anyone or look at anyone. I am supposed to go with you, but I have to finish baking more bread, so hurry on out."

It was early dawn, still almost dark. Yellow Feather grabbed two blankets, quickly packed some food and water, and hurried on down the trail till she came to the cleft. She went in and called softly to Fernando. He came right out. From the tone of her voice, he

knew something was wrong. She gave him one of the
blankets and showed him how to wear it. She led
him by the hand and hurried, almost running,
toward the fields. He kept up with her, knowing
there must be a reason they had to leave so quickly.

Dawn was breaking, and from a distance with the
early light on their backs, they looked like two
women hurrying to the fields. They hurried through
the fields and kept on going. After they left the
fields, they began erasing their tracks. They
traveled all morning until they found a cave on the
side of a hill, where they rested.

That evening they traveled again, as fast as they
could walk. Finally the next morning they saw the
village of Laguna, and they traveled around it. Two
days later they came near the village of Isleta.
Yellow Feather knew her family was known there,
so they traveled way around the village. They
traveled on, knowing that the Acoma warriors were
hunting for them. They were careful to keep out of
sight of any settlements.

One day they came to a place they decided to make their home. This place would later be called Cebolleta (Tender Onion) by the Spaniards and the wandering Dine (Navajo). It is said that descendants of Fernando de Sanchez and Yellow Feather can still be found in the towns of Belen, Albuquerque, Bernalillo and Isleta. And perhaps even Acoma.

THE LEGEND OF ATTUCK
A Massachusett Indian Story

Near the township of Framingham, Massachusetts,
was a settlement called the Village of the Praying
Indians. It was also known by the Indian name of
"Natick" by both the Indian tribes and the earlier
white settlers. Eighteen miles from Boston town,
Natick was founded by the Reverend John Eliot, a
Congregational missionary, who gathered his Indian
flock from the nearby tribes and built a mission. To
support the mission, he and his converts cut oak
lumber to sell and trade at the Boston shipyards. At
the large mission farm, the converts raised vegetables,
grains and fruits, which they also sold and traded.

The mission converts were mostly young people,
but there were some families living by the mission

who helped at the farm and lumberyard. Among these families there lived a young Massachussett Indian girl, whom the reverend called Mary, because he couldn't pronounce her Indian name.

The Reverend Eliot brought to the mission a black slave who became a very good jack-of-all-trades. As time went by, Joshua, the black slave, and Mary fell in love. Mary was already with child when she and Joshua asked the Reverend to marry them. The Reverend Eliot refused, saying they had been living in sin.

One stormy night, Joshua and Mary ran away from the mission and fled to her village, which was called Mishawum. Several days later, a manchild was born to Mary. She and Joshua named him Attuck (Small Deer). Joshua had built a house for his family, and they settled down to raise their son. But Joshua was not accepted by Mary's people. They knew he was a slave and belonged to the mission, and they feared the Reverend Eliot could make trouble for them. The

village people went out of their way to make life
unbearable for Joshua.

As Attuck grew, the village children either ignored
him, or they hit him, called him names, and threw
rocks at him. He asked his mother why the other
children did not like him or want to play with him.
Mary gathered her son in her arms. "Attuck," she
said, "my people, of which you are a part, have
been told by our elders that we must keep our
blood pure, that we must not ruin it with other
people's blood, because then our own blood would
be too weak to keep our bodies from catching their
sicknesses. Also it goes against the teachings of
Elder Brother."

Attuck did not understand why having different
blood made the other children treat him so badly.
While he was growing up, the answer remained a
puzzle. Attuck made every effort to get the people
to accept and like him. He would always turn away
from a fight, and he helped some of the elderly
people in every way he could.

One day a great sickness came to the village, and many people died of it. Joshua and Mary were struck down by the sickness and died. Those who did not catch the sickness buried the dead and burned the houses in which they died. Attuck would have been alone, an orphan, but an aunt took him in, and he was able to continue living in the village.

It was the tradition of the Massachusett tribe that all adult hunters, trappers and fishermen should select one or two orphaned boys of the tribe, from the ages of eight to fifteen, and teach them the art of hunting, fishing and trapping along with their own sons. Attuck was never chosen by any of the hunters or fishermen because of his mixed blood.

In spite of the discrimination against him, there was something in Attuck's spirit that would not let him be beaten down. He understood that he had to fend for himself or he would not survive. Now ten years old, he was taller and stronger than most of the other boys of his age. Whenever the hunting parties went out, he would follow at a distance, always keeping out of sight. From his hiding places he would watch everything the hunters did. He did the same with the fishing parties and trapping parties. Soon he was bringing home deer, rabbits, squirrels, duck and turkey. He learned to catch trout and on the seashore he caught clam and crab. He learned to trap fox, weasel and raccoon. He also learned to make his own bows, arrows and spears.

At the age of fourteen Attuck had become the best hunter, trapper and fisherman of the village. Many times when the other hunters came back empty-handed, he was able to bring down game. He and his guardian aunt never went hungry, and he always had enough to share with widows, the elderly and other orphans.

When Attuck was seventeen years old, his guardian aunt passed away from a new sickness of the lungs. Now he was alone with no place to live, as the chief ordered his aunt's dwelling burned so the sickness would also die. Attuck built himself a new house of birch bark near where his aunt's house had been.

By now Attuck had grown into a tall, muscular young man. He had the brownish-red features of his mother and his father's hair. He was the champion of the village, the strongest, the swiftest runner and the best wrestler. The other young men of the village no longer pushed him around or made fun of him. He naturally became the leader of the young people but never was a bully and did not take advantage of anyone.

The older people all liked and respected him. Old men looked up to him in the hunt for game. He was not accepted into his mother's clan, because she was dead and there was no other woman in the village to pass the clan on to him. His father was a black slave and of no clan. However, Attuck was accepted into the tribe, and he was allowed to keep his tribal name.

The maidens of the village and tribe had their eyes on him, and many called his name for all to hear, in this way expressing their choice of a husband. Some of the mothers with young daughters made excuses to ask his advice on where to hunt or pick berries. But Attuck thought only of Blue Cloud, the daughter of Brown Bear, who was the chief of the village and war chief of the tribe. Blue Cloud was the fairest of the young women of the village. Attuck knew he could not just go to Brown Bear and ask for his only daughter. He knew he had to abide by tribal tradition. He must prove he had something of value to offer. His wish came true one day.

It was late spring, the time of the year called "blueberry weather," when the delicious blueberries that grew on great bushes in the forest were ready to harvest. The berries had to be picked before the wild creatures took over the area where the bushes grew. The people didn't mind sharing the berries with small creatures such as the squirrels and birds, but they would have to hurry up and harvest as much as they could before the grizzly and brown bear came down from the mountains.

The people of that village and other nearby villages carried baskets made of birch bark into the forest. The grown people carried two large baskets, one in each hand, that each held from four to five quarts of berries. The children each carried one basket that held two quarts. Blue Cloud's mother told her to go on ahead with the others, saying she would follow later when she finished drying the fish Brown Bear had caught. Blue Cloud took down her two baskets from their holding sticks on the birch-bark wall and hurried to catch up with the others.

Starting late, she knew that most of the good berry patches would be taken. She went farther into the forest, where she would be sure to find some bushes that had not been picked. She found a good spot, not realizing how far she had gone. Nor did she realize she was out of sight and hearing of the rest of the villagers. She hurried to fill her baskets from a large bush.

As she picked she felt uneasy. She was filling one of her baskets when from the opposite side of the bush she heard a low, deep growl. Her heart skipped a beat. She stopped picking and realized she had not heard the voices of her people since she had started picking. She was all alone. A cold chill ran up and down her back as she heard something big brushing against the bush. As she backed away, she saw a huge brown bear peering over the six-foot bush, its mouth full of berries. Its black beady eyes blazed at her. It was the biggest bear she had ever seen. It came around the bush, moving toward her on its massive hind legs and extending its powerful claws like so many sharp knives. It opened its huge mouth and growled again, its black lips curling back to show needle-sharp fangs. Its foul breath stung her nostrils. She backed up slowly, then froze, staring in horror, unable to move or scream.

Just as the bear was moving in for the kill, it suddenly stopped, growling deeply, and pawed at an arrow sticking in its broad chest. Blue Cloud had not seen or heard the arrow. Another arrow swiftly struck the bear, imbedding in its throat.

The bear opened its mouth wider, spilling a gush of blood onto the ground. It swayed from side to side and charged toward Blue Cloud—it must have believed she was the one hurting it. Snapping out of the spell, she stumbled backward a few steps. She heard the swift switch-switch of two more arrows as they struck deep in the bear's body. The bear growled so loudly that the other people picking blueberries heard it. The women gathered their children and quickly moved away from the area. As the bear lunged for Blue Cloud, she heard a voice telling her to run away as fast as she could.

The bear had only one object in its savage mind, and that was to get to the creature that was running away. Blue Cloud saw Attuck rush past her to meet the bear. He plunged his stout lance into the bear's heart. He stepped back from the bear, knowing it was still dangerous even though mortally wounded. The agonized growl of the bear thundered through the forest and sent a convulsive chill through Blue Cloud.

With streams of blood pouring from its many wounds, the weakened bear took a step toward Attuck. He stood his ground, knowing the animal was near death. The bear lunged once more and fell at Attuck's feet. With one last growl, it reached for Attuck, rolled over and lay still.

Attuck kicked the bear to make sure it was dead. He retrieved his arrows and lance and went to Blue Cloud, who had fallen and was still shaking from the ordeal.

"Are you hurt?"

Trying to regain her wits, she managed to whisper, "I'm not hurt, are you all right?" She smiled at Attuck. "Where did you come from, how did you know where I was?"

"You're a foolish girl to come so far from the rest of the people, you knew that bears would be coming here." He sounded quite angry.

Blue Cloud hung her head in shame.

"I came by your dwelling, your mother told me you were picking berries. When I was searching for you, your aunt told me you had come this way. I had to find you, because on our last hunt we saw bear tracks near here. I'm glad I found you in time."

Attuck set down his weapons and smiled at Blue Cloud. "Come," he said, "I'll help you fill your baskets, then you can go home. I'll stay here to skin the bear and cut up the meat. I'll leave some of the meat at your house. Later I will tan the bearskin into a soft blanket and take it to your house. If your father accepts the bear blanket, I'll come for you before the season of the snowstorms."

Shyly smiling, Blue Cloud peered at Attuck. She was no longer afraid. Her heart was calm and her head light.

The gleam in Blue Cloud's eyes assured Attuck of her feeling for him.

She filled up her baskets with his help and proudly went on her way.

Blue Cloud stopped to answer her aunt's question about what had happened. She told her how the bear had almost killed her and how Attuck rescued her and killed the bear. Her aunt called the people around her, and soon everyone in the village knew of the bear and how Attuck had rescued Blue Cloud.

It took Attuck the rest of the day to skin and butcher the huge bear. He hung most of the meat high on a tree and later told the people where it was so they could take what they wanted. He placed the bear hide on a *travois* to drag it home and prepare it for tanning. The next day Attuck and several young men stretched and pegged the hide to the ground and scraped off all the fat and gristle. It took two weeks to tan the hide into a fine, soft blanket.

The day came when Attuck was ready to go courting. He folded the soft bearskin, and carrying it on his shoulder, he took it to Brown Bear's house. He carefully placed it at the entrance and walked away a short distance so he could keep his eye on Brown Bear's home.

All the village had been waiting for this day to see what would happen. Most of the people rallied behind Attuck, although a few who were envious stayed away. Activity in the village almost came to a standstill as the people watched and waited to see what Brown Bear would do.

The vigil lasted most of the day. Attuck was about to give up and go pick up the bearskin and take it back to his house when Brown Bear came out. He stood up straight and looked around. He saw no one but knew his people were watching, waiting to see his decision.

Attuck's heart was pounding. He thought to himself, Oh, why doesn't he make up his mind, either pick up the bearskin or kick it away?

Brown Bear turned and faced the direction where he supposed Attuck was hiding. He pointed his right hand in that direction, then pointed to the sky, at the blue clouds that floated above. It was beginning to get dark. Attuck began to sweat. He felt like he had ants crawling all over him.

Finally, just as the last color of sunlight was about to fade into twilight, Brown Bear quickly picked up the bearskin and took it inside his house.

The people came out of their hiding places and cheered. Attuck smiled, giving a long sigh of relief, and started toward his home. People began to kid him, but he didn't care. He hardly heard them, for now he knew he was accepted by Blue Cloud's family and clan. He was ready to fulfill the tradition of the tribe and supply her family with food such as deer, rabbit, squirrel, duck and fish for one cycle of seasons. Her family would then help him build a house for Blue Cloud and himself. Later the marriage ceremony would make them husband and wife for life here on earth mother and in the spirit world.

Times were good in the village. There was a fine harvest of corn, beans, squash, pumpkin, melon, nuts and berries. Plenty of smoked fish and dried meats were stored, and all the houses were prepared for the coming cold weather.

One day, one of the village men came home from a visit to Boston town, where he did odd jobs for people and worked on some of the great ships. Two days later his face was covered with red spots and he had a high fever. By the next day he was dead. The medicine man who tried to cure him became sick with the same illness, and he also died. The next day four more people died. The next day ten children died, then some older people. The fifth day was a cruel day for Attuck, for his beloved Blue Cloud became sick and died soon after. Many more people became sick and died, though some of them got well. The few who were still strong and able helped in any way they could.

Attuck buried Blue Cloud in her new bearskin blanket. He grieved for her for many days. He lost all interest in hunting and fishing and hardly ate anything.

One day the Reverend Eliot from the mission village of the Praying Indians came to offer his help and also to take Attuck back to the mission. The Reverend remembered his mother and father. He told Attuck that according to law he had to serve out his father's time as a slave at the mission. Attuck agreed and went to live at the mission for two years. Attuck didn't mind, for he felt the Reverend was a good and kind man, and Attuck had no reason to go on living in Blue Cloud's village.

Early one morning, the Reverend Adams asked Attuck to load the wagon with the oak planks they had cut and cured to sell in Boston town to the shipbuilders. When the planks were loaded, they started on their trip. Long before they arrived in Boston late that afternoon, Attuck could see the tall masts of the great sailing ships anchored in the harbor. The Reverend finished his business in the town the next day, and they started back to the mission. On their way, Attuck told the Reverend of his meeting with an American sailor called Adam and of his own wish, one day, to sail in one of those great high-masted ships. He dreamed of what it would be like to stand at the top of the highest mast, far away where there was nothing but sky and dark-blue water for as far as one could see, and even the seagulls were left behind.

Almost a year later, Attuck again went to Boston town with the Reverend Eliot. Now eighteen years old, Attuck stood a good six feet, three inches. He was a young, light, red-black giant, who could carry a two-hundred-pound sack of grain and pick up a heavy oak log that took two grown men to lift. He did twice the work of any of the men around the mission farm.

Attuck found Adam, the American sailor, again and went with him and his friends to the Blue Boar Tavern to have something to eat and drink. In the tavern they noticed a group of at least twenty drunk and noisy English soldiers—called "Red Coats"—and a few local people. The Red Coats loudly insulted and taunted the American sailors, who ignored them and took seats in a far corner of the tavern.

When the sergeant of the Red Coats began abusing
and harassing the young barmaid who came by
with a tray of foaming ale for the Americans,
Attuck moved so fast from his place at the table
that he was across the room before anyone realized
he had risen from his seat. He grasped the sergeant
by the collar of his red jacket and the seat of his
blue pants and heaved him over his head onto the
heavy oak table. A free-for-all ensued between the
Red Coats and the ten Americans. It did not last
long. With Attuck in the lead, the Americans
charged into the soldiers and soon scattered and
chased them out of the tavern. The proprietor went
in search of the sheriff. The barmaid warned the
American sailors that the sheriff would come to
arrest Attuck.

The sailors urged Attuck to go aboard their ship,
where they could hide him from the sheriff.

Attuck found the Reverend Eliot and told him what
had happened. The Reverend gave him his blessing
and permission to go, telling him to hurry before

the sheriff came for him. The captain of the ship was pleased with Attuck and enlisted him in the American Navy. That night the ship, the U.S.S. America, sailed with the tide on a two-year voyage around the world.

On his return to Boston town on the U.S.S. America two years later, Attuck found everything much changed. The Reverend Eliot's mission had been abandoned. The Reverend and his wife had left following an Indian war when the local white people had turned against all Indians. Many of the Indians had fled to the land of the Massachusetts and to Canada, the land of the Cree. Others were captured and taken to different tribes. From local people in Boston, Attuck learned that relations between the British and the colonists were getting worse and worse. The Red Coats looked down on the local people and often mistreated them. The colonists were angry because of high taxes, lack of freedom of speech, and restrictions on trade and land ownership. Fed up with the government that ruled them from overseas, the colonists talked of rebellion.

At the end of their shore leave, Attuck and the other sailors reported back aboard their ship. For the next few days they were kept busy getting the ship ready for another voyage.

On March 5, 1770, in the late afternoon, when all the shipboard tasks were done, Attuck and the other sailors had liberty and went ashore to town. Attuck and Adam noticed more people than usual in the old state square. Nearby they heard a man urging a group of colonists not to pay any more tax until the laws were changed. They saw Red Coats, fully armed, break through the crowds, arresting the leaders and dispersing the people. A company of Red Coat officers was gathered in front of the square, taking down names of people who had been singled out by a traitor. Most of the colonists in the square were young people. Some of them dared the Red Coats to come and get them. The tension between them was like a powder keg, ready to explode.

Soon more people came to the square. Attuck and Adam and other sailors from the U.S.S. America

were at the front of the crowd facing the Red
Coats. The Red Coats were becoming very nervous.
Attuck heard one of them call the colonists "scum
and whipped dogs."

A young boy threw an apple, which hit the chief
Red Coat officer in the chest. The officer angrily
faced the crowd and yelled, "You scum! Who
threw that?"

No one answered until the young boy stepped
forward. "I did," he said boldly.

The officer lunged forward to grab him, but the boy
ran into the crowd. The officer ordered his men to
fix their bayonets, disperse the crowd and bring the
boy to him.

The Red Coats advanced to the crowd with fixed
bayonets and halted in a tight square formation.
The crowd refused to retreat. The officer ordered his
men to kneel and aim their muskets at the people.

Attuck could sense the rising anger of the officer in
command. Knowing some of the women and children

would be killed, he said to Adam, "They are going to start killing people, let's get them first."

Thus said, Attuck, Adam and two other sailors rushed the Red Coats. The officer gave the order to fire, and Attuck took the full volley in his body. He fell to the ground, dead. Adam and the other two sailors were also killed as the crowd quickly scattered. The Red Coats continued to fire at the fleeing crowd, killing many other people.

Attuck lay dead in front of the Red Coat formation. He had become the first Native American to die in the colonists' struggle against the English.

HUMMINGBIRD & WHITE OTTER

A Yurok Love Story

In the land of the Yurok, in the northwest part of
what is now the state of California, there was a
village called Weilspus. In this village lived a pretty
girl who was given the name of Hummingbird by
her grandfather. She was raised in the tradition of
the Yurok. In this tribe a young maiden's future
depended mostly on her marrying a man of wealth,
even if the man already had a wife or even two
wives. Sometimes a poor family would send their
daughter to a wealthy man's house in hopes he
would take their daughter as a wife. Whether
married or not, Yurok women did the work of
preparing food, gathering seeds, digging roots,
harvesting acorns and weaving baskets.

Hummingbird's father was a wealthy man, and his family was important in the village. Before her father had become wealthy he had been a canoe maker and had borrowed many strings of seashells from a friend in order to trade for more goods. Hummingbird was three years old when her father's friend started pressing him on his debt. To avoid paying him back in strings of seashells, her father offered to give Hummingbird to his friend's young son in marriage, without any payment, to cancel the debt. The two men agreed on the bargain: The children were to marry when they came of age.

When Hummingbird reached the age of maturity, she was initiated. She was required to sit silent in her house for ten days with her back to the center fire in the house. She was forbidden to move about. If she had to scratch her head, she had to use a bone piece specially made for scratching. Once a day she had to bring in a supply of firewood. On her way in and out of the house she could not look at anyone or even glance to the right or left. It was important to fast a long time, because the longer

she could go without food, the more food she would
have in her life. She could eat on the fourth day
only at a place chosen for her, near the river, where
the roar of the river would drown out all the other
sounds. If by chance she heard an animal or bird,
she had to stop eating.

She was required to bathe every evening. The first
night she bathed one time, the second night two
times, the third night three times and so on, until
the eighth night, when she poured water all over
herself eight times. On the ninth night she bathed
ten times. At the end of that day she sat by the
riverbank while the village children washed her
back. Her mother laid ten sticks on the sand and
told her she would have that many sons. Then her
mother placed ten sticks in a row on her back and
said, "Those will be your daughters."

During this ceremony Hummingbird wore a skirt of
shredded maple-tree bark. After that, as a young
maiden, she would wear a front-and-back buckskin
apron that reached to her ankles and a round

basket-woven cap on her head. Like all the
women, in cold weather she would wear a cloak
or blanket made of two deerskins sewn together.
For ceremonial dances she would wear a white
buckskin skirt with long fringes and hanging
clamshells that jingled when she moved. Because
she was part of a wealthy family, her skirt would
have rows of smooth obsidian crystals that tinkled
as she walked. On her feet she wore one-piece
front-seamed moccasins. In winter she wore a fur
cape. As a maiden, she could now wear her long
black hair gathered in two masses falling in front
of her breast and held together with strips of
mink fur and woodpecker scalps. On her chin
below her lower lip, she had the vertical tattoo
stripes of her tribe.

Hummingbird was a pretty girl, a good hard
worker—a good seed gatherer, root digger and
acorn harvester. Married men began to ask about
her. Unmarried young men made all kinds of
excuses to hang around her home and follow her
when she went seed-gathering with the other

women. But Hummingbird had eyes only for White
Otter, a young man who stayed in the background.

Like all Yurok boys, when he was about four years
of age, White Otter was sent outside to talk to
every new moon. He would run a short distance
from his house toward the east. There, near the
river, was a large rock. He would climb the rock
and call to the moon, "Grandfather, look at me, I
am growing tall and strong, I am going to be big."
In Yurok this was called getting moon-power
guidance. If the young boy were noticed by one of
the world spirits who saw that the boy was serious,
the spirit became the boy's guardian.

When White Otter reached the age of eight years,
he was initiated into manhood. He was first
whipped with a bowstring and then had to jump
into an ice-cold stream. Going through this
ceremony would make him tough and able to
withstand injuries and sickness.

White Otter was now a fine, strong young man. And
he was handsome. Many of the young maidens of

the village slyly looked at him, but they knew he
liked Hummingbird.

So many men wanted her for a wife that
Hummingbird had become the talk of the village.
When her father's friend heard of this, he
demanded he bring her to his house and live up to
their bargain. Hummingbird did not want to
become the boy's wife and refused to go. Every day
her father demanded she go with him, saying that
if she did not, he would lose everything.

One evening, after the women had come back from
seed-gathering, she slipped away into the wooded
hills, where she knew White Otter would be
waiting. She heard his whistle signal, and they
found each other. She rushed into his arms, and
he held her tight. There and then they made
their plans.

That night, when everyone had gone to bed, she
slipped out, and at his signal, they met and
traveled quickly away from the village. Carrying
their buckskin blankets, some acorn meal, and

dried fish, White Otter and Hummingbird followed the river toward the east.

When they were out of sight of the village, White Otter said, "We will go to the land of the Paiute, who live to the east in the desert. If we are wrong in what we are doing, it will be decided against us and not against our families." According to Yurok laws, any claims against them were theirs alone. If they were caught, White Otter would have to pay the man Hummingbird was to marry with a year of work or hunting, and she would have to marry him.

They traveled the rest of the night and all the next day. Late that afternoon they found a cave in the mountains and rested there. White Otter told Hummingbird to stay hidden in the cave while he backtracked to erase their tracks, for he was sure the village people would come after them.

She waited all day for White Otter to return. When night came and he still had not come, she became afraid. She worried—perhaps the people had caught him and taken him back. Maybe he needed her help

and she should try to go back and find him.
Hummingbird didn't know what to do. She heard
coyotes howling and yelping, and she moved farther
into the cave. "Oh, where is he?" she thought.

The coyotes became silent. Hummingbird had a
strong feeling that a mountain lion was close by.
She dared not build a fire for fear the village scouts
might see it and capture her and take her back to
her father's friend's dwelling. She feared White
Otter was already dead. After a little while the
coyotes started howling and yelping once more, and
she thought the mountain lion had gone away.

When the coyotes stopped again, she felt the
mountain lion close by.

Facing the entrance of the cave, she could see a
little light from the outside. Her heart began to
beat faster, and a ripple ran up and down her
neck. She couldn't see the body of the lion, but
she could see its green, glaring eyes near the
entrance. Fear spread through her body, and she
was afraid to move.

Finally, the glaring eyes disappeared and she breathed a sigh of relief.

Suddenly the eyes appeared again. She called out as loud as she could, "White Otter, where are you?" When she stepped deeper into the cave, she felt a rock pressing against her moccasin. Slowly she bent as if to sit down, still watching the cave entrance, and reached for the rock. Holding it tight, she slowly stood up and threw the rock with all her might where she thought the lion was. She knew she had missed it, but the rock bounced against the cave wall, making a clanking sound. The green, glaring eyes disappeared.

She felt around the cave floor for more rocks. As she found them, she threw them at the entrance and gave a loud yell at the same time. After a while she heard the coyotes howling and yelping, and she calmed down. Just before dawn she fell asleep.

She awoke with a jerk as she felt a hand shaking her shoulder. She opened her eyes wide, still heavy with sleep, to see White Otter standing over her. In a moment she was wide awake. She stood up and smiled at him, almost crying. Happy but a little angry too, she asked, "What happened, where did you go?"

White Otter gathered her in his arms and said, "I was covering our trail and making a new one that leads to the land of the Wahos. That way, whoever is chasing us will have to go into the high desert, where it is windy, and the trail will blow away. Now we must get far away from here before the doctors from our village are able to kill me." White Otter knew the rattlesnake doctors from the Yurok villages would try to send snakes to bite him.

"We will travel to the land of the Paiute," he said. "They will let us live among them, and someday we will come back to our people."

MILLIE
A Seminole Indian Maiden

For some years the U.S. government and the white settlers in the Florida Territory had tried to persuade the Seminole Indian clans to sign treaties that would have resulted in the Seminoles' losing most of their rich farmlands. Some clans had been tricked in this way into selling part of their lands. Meanwhile many skirmishes were taking place between the Seminoles and the white settlers. Finally the U.S. government sent the Army under the command of General Andrew Jackson to the Seminole country to keep the peace.

Two Indian villages held out the strongest against the signing of the treaties. These villages were known as the red or bloody villages. The French settlers called them "red stick" or *"baton rouge"* villages because the village people had sunk tall poles of pine into the ground and painted them red. The red poles announced the villages' state of war with the white settlers and the U.S. Army, as well as with any Indians who were friendly to the white settlers or helped the U.S. Army.

The warriors from these two villages were known as the most courageous of all the Seminoles. A fierce old warrior by the name of Hillis Hadjo, or Francis the Prophet, was the chief of Mikasuki, one of the red-stick villages.

In 1817 war began in earnest. All the Seminole clans had been called in to the two red-stick villages to prepare for war, and fierce battles were fought between the Seminoles and the U.S. Army. All Seminole children in mission schools in St. Augustine and other missions were taken back to their villages.

Chief Hillis had a beautiful sixteen-year-old daughter whose name was Water Flower, but she had been given the name "Millie" at the mission. Millie and her mother belonged to the Black Bear (Ara) Clan.

One day Millie and her mother had gone out into the forest in search of the type of holly from which "Indian black drink" was made. The leaves and tender roots were to be gathered and dried and then made into tea to use as medicine. Millie and her mother found some shrubs, and her mother was about to pick leaves when a timber rattlesnake struck at her. It missed her, but as she backed away she tripped and fell down, breaking her leg.

Millie was helping her mother when they were surprised by one of General Jackson's white soldier scouts. Both women were scared, because they knew if they were captured by soldiers, they would be taken away and sold as slaves to the Spaniards. Millie tried to fight the soldier, but he was too strong for her. When Millie quieted down, the soldier said, "I won't hurt you, I want to help you. I can help her."

Millie sat down and watched as the soldier set and made rough splints for her mother's broken leg. As he worked he kept looking at Millie. He was thinking, "What a beautiful girl."

When he had done all he could do and was ready to move on, he was surprised and surrounded by Chief Hillis's warriors. They were ready to kill him there and then, when Chief Hillis came up and decided to hold off. The soldier was taken prisoner and brought to the village.

Before they took him away, Millie asked the prisoner what he was called. He looked at her and replied, "I am Private Duncan McKrimmon."

The next day, after a short council meeting, it was decided to put Private McKrimmon to death. Chief Hillis ordered the prisoner to be burned at the stake. A big feast and ceremonial dance began the following day and continued through the night.

The next day Private McKrimmon's head was shaved, and he was led to the center pole in the village and tied to it. Logs and brush were piled all around him.

Chief Hillis was about to give the signal for the fire to be lit, when suddenly Millie rushed to her father, fell to her knees and begged for Private McKrimmon's life. She reminded him that Private McKrimmon had saved her mother, at considerable risk to himself. Because this was war, Chief Hillis shook her off and was once more about to give the signal when Millie ran to the pile of logs and brush and threatened to jump into the fire.

Chief Hillis had great love for his only daughter and could not bear to see her die by his own hands. So Private McKrimmon was spared and taken down from the stake. He was kept a prisoner until he was taken to San Marco and traded to the Spanish for a barrel of whiskey. The Spaniards later gave him back his freedom. Private McKrimmon returned to the Army, but he never forgot Millie.

After Chief Hillis Hadjo died, General Andrew Jackson moved in great force against the Seminoles

at the Battle of Horseshoe Bend. One of the first
villages to be attacked was Mikasuki, where Millie
still lived with her mother. The village warriors
who survived the attack, as well as the women,
children and old men of the village, were taken
prisoner. Sick and starving, they were moved to
Fort St. Mark. Palm-leaf huts had been put up in a
compound near the camp, and rations of rice,
beans, sugar and coffee were issued to the prisoners
each week.

It was known at the fort that the old chief's
daughter was among the prisoners. One of the
sentries at the fort knew McKrimmon and the story
of how Millie had saved his life. The sentry had
looked at all the girls in the compound, wondering
which one she could be. He noticed that one girl
was prettier than all the others, and he thought she
had to be Millie.

The sentry asked his commanding officer if he
could visit another outpost, the one where
McKrimmon was doing duty. He was granted leave

to go and soon found McKrimmon. He told McKrimmon he was sure that Millie was one of the prisoners at his post.

The next day McKrimmon went to the prison compound, but he stayed out of sight. He waited until the following morning when the prisoners lined up for their rations. He had tried to forget Millie, but he couldn't. He had often dreamed of her and wondered if he would ever see her again. Now that he believed he had found her, his heart was beating fast. But when all the prisoners were lined up and counted, he didn't see Millie. He was disappointed and sick at heart.

He was about to turn away and go back to his post when Millie and her mother came out and lined up with the rest. He had not seen her in over a year, but she was as pretty as he had pictured her all that time. He kept her in sight as she and her mother went back to their huts with their rations.

McKrimmon went to the sergeant of the guard and asked to see Millie. When he told the sergeant the story, the sergeant agreed to let him in. When Millie saw McKrimmon coming toward her, her heart began to swell up in her chest, and she could hardly breathe. But she felt nervous and shy, and as he came up she hung her head.

McKrimmon said, "Millie, I've been hoping I'd find you. I don't know how to say this, but I want you, I want to marry you. Do you understand what I am saying?"

Millie looked up at him and said, "I understand why you are saying this. You are saying this because you feel sorry for me, you feel you have to repay me for your life. You don't owe me anything. Besides, you are my enemy, you are a white man."

McKrimmon replied, "Millie, I am not saying my life belongs to you because you saved me, or that I feel sorry for you and your people. This has nothing to do with payment. I am offering you my love, for I do love you."

Millie replied, "You go back and think hard about what you say. Come back in fourteen days. If you love me like you say, I will wait for you."

He promised her he would be back and told her that he would leave the Army and take her away somewhere out west.

That year of 1818 many Seminoles, especially women and children who had been captured near Fort St. Mark, were taken to Fort Gadsden. Millie and her mother were among them. There they joined Creek, Choctaw, Chickasaw and Cherokee prisoners who were also sick and starving. The next day was the first day of the Trail of Tears from Fort Gadsen to the Territory of Oklahoma.

On the fourteenth day, as he had promised, Duncan returned to Fort St. Mark, only to find Millie gone. He asked where she had been taken. He was informed that she, with other Indian prisoners, was on her way to the new Indian country in the Oklahoma Territory.

The Trail of Tears was easy to follow. Every night, those prisoners who died were buried along the trail. For some tribes there were burial mounds; for others the burial places were erased, but there were enough burial mounds to mark the trail. Duncan checked each one with a heavy heart, afraid of what he might find. He knew Millie's people and the other Indians were sick and starved, and this long forced march would kill many more.

Duncan was A.W.O.L., and he needed to find Millie before the Army caught up with him. She had promised to wait for him. He knew she loved him, and he knew he would always love her.

Two days later Duncan was captured by the Army. He was taken back to an Army stockade and sentenced to two years of hard labor.

Millie and her mother reached the new Indian Territory. Millie's mother died the first year in the new territory. She had been urging Millie to marry, for she was sure Duncan was not coming for her. But every night Millie would walk a mile or so back along the trail, hoping to see Duncan coming. She would sit down on a log and call to him and softly cry.

After a year's time Millie lost hope that he would come. She married a Seminole warrior, and they moved away and were never seen in the Indian Territory again.

After serving his two-year sentence, Duncan also disappeared from the area. Someone at a trading post had told him Millie died and no one knew where she was buried.

ENEMY LOVE
An Akimel O'Odham (Pima) Story

There was great commotion and excitement one day
in the main camp of Nachez, the great Chiricahua
Apache chief. Nachez and his warriors had returned
from a raid in the land of the Akimels in present-day
Arizona. They had brought back horses, mules,
baskets of corn, beans, two young Akimel girls and
one young man sixteen years of age who had been
surprised and captured while hunting a stray horse.
The raiders did not want to kill the young man, whose
name was Tail Feathers (Bahbhai), because he would
be worth more alive to the raiders. He could be taken
to Mexico and traded for guns and bullets.

The two Akimel girls were given to families who
had need for them. For the time being, Tail

Feathers was given to an elderly couple who were in need of someone to help them. He was to gather food such as acorns, wild seeds, wild red berries, mescal plants and walnuts, as well as firewood.

At first the old couple were not too sure they had made a good choice in asking for him. But they needed someone, and after talking about it together, they had decided to take their chances on him.

Tail Feathers had one single thought in his mind, and that was to escape the first chance he had. It would not be easy to escape, because he was watched. A sentry came by every once in a while to check on him. Tail Feathers knew that the sentry had been ordered to shoot to kill if he tried to escape. He knew he must wait and be ready and not make any trouble or attempt to escape until he had a good plan.

Tail Feathers was a strong, fine-looking young man, and before long the old couple came to like and depend on him. Be-mah, the old woman, never scolded him or whipped him. Instead she made a place for him in their wickiup and started teaching him her language. He was a good student and soon was learning to speak and understand it.

Be-mah also taught him how to make acorn soup *(e-too)* by grinding acorn with salt and cooking it with deer bones that still had lots of meat on them. She taught him how to make a sweet drink *(cha-go-asa)* from wild red berries. She taught him how to make Apache tamales *(be-aa-elsta-a)* and Apache bread *(chi-yo-st-aay)*, and how to cook mescal cabbage *(no-do)*. The old man taught him how to skin and cut up the deer brought to them by one of the hunters. But most of the time Tail Feathers was sent from their wickiup to harvest acorns, wild walnuts, wild red berries and mescal plants with the women and children of the village.

Tail Feathers did everything he was told to do. He didn't argue or fight back. If he made any kind of trouble, they would be sure to guard him more closely. Every time he went out with the food gatherers, he looked for the best way to escape. He studied every possible escape route and kept an eye open for good places to hide. He learned all he could of the wild food plants. As he worked, he listened to what the women and girls were saying. As he grew skilled in understanding their language, he learned more and more about what was going on in the village.

Tail Feathers remembered how many days had passed since he had been captured and brought to the Apache camp in the month of February, called *Auppa I' iwagithag* (the month of cottonwood leavings). Now the cottonwood leaves would be big, bright and green, and it would be warm at home. He thought of home, his parents, and his friends, and his heart was beating slow as he longed to be there. But he knew he must await his chance to escape.

One day he was told to go with a large group to harvest the mescal plant roots that grew in the lower lands. As he followed the group of women and children, he saw an older girl at the front of the group. She was a very pretty girl who seemed to be well respected by all the others. The group found a good patch of mescal plants, and they dug and harvested as much as they could carry in their burden baskets.

When they came back to camp late that afternoon, Tail Feathers took his share of mescal roots to the old couple's wickiup. They came out to help him prepare the roots. As they worked, he told the woman of the pretty girl he had seen that day. The woman smiled and said, "That pretty girl's name is Ba-go-szo-na, and she is the daughter of Chief Nachez. She is not married yet. Many of the young warriors are looking at her, and some have visited her and have had their parents talk to her parents. I must tell you to be careful and stay away from her. You are a good person, but you are a prisoner of our people. I heard Nachez say that the warrior who claims his daughter will have to give him horses and white buckskin. Where will you get horses and buckskins?"

Tail Feathers had no answer. He went outside to gather firewood.

The next day the same group went out to harvest mescal. As Tail Feathers began digging up plants, his thoughts wandered back to Ba-go-szo-na. He knew it was no use hoping to win her for his wife, because he was their enemy. As he worked he felt someone was watching him, not the sentry but someone hiding nearby. When he bent down to dig a plant, he could feel someone's eyes on him. He looked around. He could see the sentry who watched over the group, but he was some distance away. Tail Feathers still felt there was someone close by in the bushes who was keeping out of sight.

As he bent over to dig another plant, a pebble hit him on his back. He wanted to straighten up and look around, but he held off and just went on digging. Then a larger pebble hit him between his shoulder blades. Still he didn't look up. He heard a giggle, and he knew it had to be a girl. He

didn't know what to think or what to do. He was
surprised, wondering if this girl was teasing him
or trying to get him in trouble. He had to find
out, but he had to be careful. He couldn't afford
to get mixed up with a girl of his enemies. And his
people had said that Apache women were very
possessive of their men and would fight like
wildcats to keep them.

He started to move a little closer to the bushes.
When he saw the sentry coming toward him,
he went on with his digging. The sentry came
by and looked at him. He pointed at him with
his short lance and said, "Old women's work,"
not knowing that Tail Feathers could understand
the language. The sentry moved on. Tail
Feathers had been tempted to jump him, but
he knew that would be foolish. He kept on
digging, for he was sure the sentry would be
watching him from some other place. Tail
Feathers moved farther toward the bushes and
started digging in a new spot.

It wasn't long before he heard someone making noise in the bushes behind him. He was puzzled. He stood up and looked around, but he still saw no one. Why was this girl following him like a shadow? What was she up to? Well, he thought he'd find out who she was and what she was up to. He slowly bent down and started digging. At the same time he carefully slipped a stone into his hand. He stood up and moved to his left until he was behind a large bush. He quickly threw the rock in a high arc so that it fell a short distance behind her hiding place. Waiting until he heard the rock hit the ground, he rushed around the large bush where he knew the girl would be.

He bumped into her just as she was rushing to see what had made the noise. The girl fell down on her rear. When she looked up at Tail Feathers, her fierce, blazing eyes bore into him. She was even prettier than he had thought. He smiled as he offered his hand to help her up but she slapped his hand away. She got up on her own and stood in front of him. Her mouth quivered as she said,

112

"You Akimel slave, you are called Tail Feathers.
The old woman Be-mah says you are a good man,
a good worker. Why don't you try to escape? I can
help you."

Tail Feathers was surprised. Why did she want him
to escape? Was the camp moving to another area?
What would happen to him? The other night he
had heard that Chato, another Chiricahua chief,
was in camp to plan raids on ranches in the
territory. The warriors would raid in small bands,
in different areas, and all young men were to go on
these raids to learn the art of Apache war. She
seemed surprised when he asked her in her own
language why she wanted him to escape.

She laughed lightly and replied, "I have been
watching you every day because I like you, I want
to be with you. I know the other girls here all look
at you and smile. Perhaps you look at them too,
perhaps you want them instead of me—I could
scratch their eyes out. But if you do not like me, I
will not follow you anymore."

Tail Feathers replied, "It's not that I don't like you. I do like you, you are the prettiest girl I have ever seen. But don't you understand I am a slave, a prisoner? Your people and my people are enemies. What can we do? Where can we go?" Without waiting for her to answer, he said, "At home I was almost a warrior, I passed all of my tests except one. I still need to kill an enemy. We have three enemies, the Mohaves, the Tontos and your people. I don't want to have to kill any of your people, because of you and the old couple I stay with, but I still want to go back to my people. I will escape the first chance I get." Tail Feathers looked around to see if the sentry were close by, but couldn't see him. He went on in a low voice, "Now I will ask you, will you go with me when I escape? Can you leave your parents, leave your people and go with me? I know you are the daughter of Nachez, the great chief of your people. I know he will chase us and have me killed if they catch us."

Ba-go-szo-no replied, "Yes, I will go with you, but will your people accept me?"

Tail Feathers replied, "Some of them will not like you, but we will have the help of my parents. Our elders do not believe in mixing our blood with the blood of any of our enemies. But there are some children of mixed blood in our tribe."

Ba-go-szo-no said, "I will tell my mother that I go to visit Be-mah, the old woman where you live, to ask her about a certain story. We must always meet in secret to make our plans to escape." She moved away quickly when she noticed the sentry was not anywhere to be seen. She knew he could be coming their way.

Tail Feathers began digging. It wasn't long before he heard the sentry coming up behind him. The sentry motioned for him to go where the others were gathered. Tail Feathers picked up his burden basket and made his way back to the group. When everyone was ready, they went back to camp.

Back at the wickiup, Be-mah noticed that Tail Feathers was tense and silent. She said, "You

115

bring some more wood but don't come back
right away. Wait out there and listen to the
nighthawk, then come back and tell me what you
heard." She thought it would help him
calm down.

Tail Feathers went out to his favorite place, a large
rock where he would sit almost every night and
dream of home and go over his escape plans. The
rock where he sat could be seen by everyone in the
camp, and the people were used to seeing him there
when he was not working.

It was now almost dark. He had been sitting for a
while when he felt a pebble hit his back. His heart
quickened. He strained to listen, waiting very
quietly. At last he heard Ba-go-szo-na whisper,
"Tail Feathers, I am here, I have something to tell
you. Walk toward the small willow tree behind you.
Be careful, don't try to hide, just walk over and
stand by the tree."

Tail Feathers walked to the tree and waited there.

Ba-go-szo-na began to speak in a low voice. "Tail Feathers, we have to make our escape soon, because Chato and my father are arguing over you. My father wants to take you on his raids, but Chato wants to trade you. Tomorrow the two-day war ceremony will start. The crown dancers will come out, and the medicine man will bless the warriors. Chato's daughter will be the princess. I don't have to help, but I will dance. I have packed some corn, dried berries and dried meat—they are hidden up in a tree near the creek. We can slip away in the middle of the last night—the warriors will be too full of *tulipi* to chase us.

"We have to watch out for Ya-ba-kish. He is one of the young warriors who had his parents ask my parents if they would arrange a marriage between our two families. My father told them to wait till after the raids, and since then Ya-ba-kish has been following me, keeping out of sight. I think he has seen us, I'm not sure, but he is around somewhere."

"I don't want to hurt him," Tail Feathers replied. "But if he gets in our way I will knock him down and tie him up. By the time he gets loose or someone finds him, we should be far away."

Tail Feathers listened for Ya-ba-kish but did not sense anyone nearby. "I know a good way out of the camp," he said quickly. "I was training to be a scout, and I can read signs and trails. We will not go the way I was brought in—they will expect us to do that. We will go another way and travel as fast as we can by night and hide out in the daytime. Your people are good trackers and hunters, so they will be hard to fool."

Ba-go-szo-no said, "I will go back now before they miss me. Stay by the rock awhile longer and then go back so they can see you. If I hear anything else I'll find a way to tell you."

The next morning Tail Feathers was told to gather firewood for the night dance. The sentry went out with Tail Feathers to keep a watch over him, and

Yo-ba-kish was keeping an eye on him from a distance.

As he gathered firewood, Tail Feathers could feel Ba-go-szo-no was somewhere nearby but out of sight. All day he thought of her and even pictured her as his wife in his home. He wanted very much to take her home with him. He knew she liked him, and it didn't matter to him that his people and her people were enemies. He figured if his people and his family didn't trust her or like her, he would take her to the land of the lower Akimel O'Odham on the Santa Cruz River.

That night when the ceremony fires were lighted, Ba-go-szo-no came to Tail Feathers and told him that her father, Chief Nachez, had decided to take him to Mexico and trade him for bullets. They would have to escape during the last night of the ceremony—it would be their only chance.

The first day of the ceremony Tail Feathers was told to stay close to the wickiup, where he could be seen easier. He did as he was told, spending the first day and night of the ceremony in plain sight near the wickiup. The second day would be the longest, and the second night would be the hardest to wait out. Since the dancing would be at its height and everyone would be there, no one would be left to keep watch on him—even the old woman and man would be at the dance. But he stayed where he could be seen if someone were to check up on him.

He was waiting for Ba-go-szo-no when he heard footsteps coming fast up behind him. It was not Ba-go-szo-no—he felt the hair on his neck ripple and knew he was in danger. He turned quickly to see Ya-ba-kish rushing him with a knife in his hand, Tail Feathers sidestepped him and hit him a hard blow in his jaw that knocked him out. Just then Ba-go-szo-no came by the wickiup. She helped Tail Feathers carry Ya-ba-kish away into some brush. They tied him up and put a gag in his mouth. Ba-go-szo-no ran back to the wickiup and picked up her bundle. From there Tail Feathers took the lead, and they hurried away from camp as fast as they could.

After they traveled all night and part of the next day, Tail Feathers slipped back to cover up their tracks and trail. They hid until nightfall in a clump of bushes. Ba-go-szo-no kept watch while Tail Feathers rested. From there they traveled on for three nights, hiding by day. One morning while on watch, Ba-go-szo-no saw some of her people's warriors searching for them. But Tail Feathers had covered their tracks well, and the warriors headed back without finding them.

Early on the fourth day, after traveling all night, they came to a river in the land of the Akimels. They were home! They hurried on until at last they came to Tail Feathers' village. His people, who had given up hope of seeing him again, welcomed him joyfully. His parents welcomed Ba-go-szo-na, and the two young people were soon married.

At village gatherings, they were always invited to tell the story of their escape from the camp of the great Apache Chief Nachez.

MARIA'S LOVE
A Cochiti Story

It was a beautiful clear morning for the *tablita* dance. The singing and the drumming had already begun. Soon from the kiva came the first group of dancers—two men dancers in the lead, followed by two women dancers.

Maria, a young Pueblo maiden of sixteen, was one of the two women dancers. She had been chosen to dance in the leading position because she had done well in the other dances. Behind the two women came the man who had the high honor of carrying the long pole with the banner known as the holy flag of the sun. Behind him came the other dancers.

The entire group circled the plaza before they entered it. The men danced rhythmically in

unison in the center of the plaza, while the
women danced more gracefully following the men.
At a certain beat of the drum and change in the
song, the dancers moved into a double line, men
in one, women in the other facing them. As the
drums beat slowly, they all faced toward the east
for one song, then they turned around, keeping
time to the song and facing to the west. They
danced this way to each song in each round. The
war captain had decided that each group would
sing five songs.

The men dancers wore white kilts embroidered
on the fringes with symbols. Their chests and
arms were painted white, and fox skins hung
from their waists. Their long black hair fell
back on their shoulders, and on top of their heads
they wore tufts of green parrot feathers. They
wore high-top moccasins with skunk fur tied
around their ankles. In his right hand each man
held a gourd rattle and in his left hand a bough
of green spruce.

The women each wore her black *manta*, a cotton belt around her waist, and on her head she wore a *tablita* headdress of rainbow design. The women's faces and arms were painted white. In each hand they held a bough or several twigs of spruce.

As the line of women dancers faced to the east, Maria happened to look toward the alley between the two rows of houses. There stood a young man staring at her. He wore a bright-purple silk shirt, buckskin pants, high moccasins, and a red-and-white cotton sash around his waist. His long black hair hung in braids on his chest. She kept looking at him and he at her. For a moment he turned away, and she quickly lowered her head, but she could still see him. He looked back at her and smiled. She slowly raised her head, their eyes met, and she caught his smile. It was a nice smile, and her heart seemed to stop. She smiled back at him, and at that moment she lost the rhythm of the dance. She felt embarrassed and wanted to leave the dance line.

He in turn knew he had caused her to miss her steps, so he quickly moved away. She looked for him again, but he was nowhere in sight.

When her dancing group was replaced for a rest, she hurried toward her home, feeling confused. The young man stepped out in front of her from around the corner of a house. She stopped where she was and didn't try to go around him. He smiled and said, "I like you, you're very pretty and you dance very well."

Maria's face brightened and she felt her heart thumping. But her feeling suddenly turned to fear, and she said, "You are making fun of me, I hate you, what are you doing here?"

The boy looked puzzled and hurt. He turned around and went his way.

Maria continued on to her home. She went into her room and lay down on her back, staring at the ceiling. Tears began to cloud her eyes. "Why was I so mean to him?" she thought. "I've never seen him before, and yet I feel like I've been waiting for him for a long time. He's the one I see in the clouds, the one I feel in the wind and see in my dream catcher. He was so nice and so friendly, what's wrong with me?"

The other girl dancer, whose name was Juanita, came to see her. "Maria, did you see that good-looking boy out in the plaza?" she asked. "The one in the purple silk shirt? He sure is good-looking. If you see him you might fall in love with him, I know I have. I sure want to know where he is from. Did you see him?"

Maria replied, "No, and I don't care to see him. You say he is good-looking, then perhaps he is a witch, a *Ka-nat-yai-ya*." The girls knew that a *Ka-nat-yai-ya* could appear as any kind of human, or animal, or bird, or even as a fireball. Maria said, "A *Ka-nat-yai-ya* can appear as someone from another tribe, so you should to be careful."

Juanita replied, "I don't care, I think I love him."

Maria replied, "How can you love someone you saw just one time?"

Juanita answered, "I don't know, but I saw someone like him in my dream catcher."

Maria went to the plaza, hoping to see the boy. She saw him where they had first met, and she went up to him, her heart beating fast. Before she knew what she was doing, she said "Go on, go someplace, don't watch us dance, go to your village. Don't look at me, I'm not like the other girls."

She turned around and went back to her home. Her head was whirling, and she didn't feel like dancing. She couldn't understand why she said what she said to him, because in her heart she knew she wanted him. She decided to go out once more to find him and tell him she didn't mean what she had said.

She found him again at the same place. She went up to him, but before she could say a word,

127

he looked at her with a stern face and said, "I came to see the dance, I didn't come to see you, you're not the only girl around here." He turned around and before she could reply, he hurried away from her.

Maria was surprised and hurt. She moved on, walking around in a daze. She remembered what Juanita had said about the boy, and she thought Juanita might try to get him. She could not let Juanita get him.

She swallowed her pride and began asking people if they had seen him and if they knew who he was. She asked an Acoma woman, but she didn't know. She asked a Zia woman, but she didn't know, she asked a Santo Domingo woman who didn't know, and she asked a Laguna woman who didn't know either. She went home disgusted and mad at herself. How could anyone be so dumb and blind and not know it was love she felt?

She knew she loved him, and she even thought of marriage, though her people would strongly disapprove of her marrying into another pueblo and tribe. They wanted girls to marry within their own pueblo.

Maria was very beautiful and a fine, hard-working girl, and she had received proposals since she was very young. The father of each boy had come to her house to talk to her parents, and marriage had been proposed. When the family was well off, they offered her parents silver jewelry, shawls, buckskin and sheep. Her parents tried talking her into accepting, but Maria had turned down every proposal. And now she had met the one she knew she loved and had chased him away. She was determined to find him.

The next day her aunt came to visit. Maria told her about the boy and how she felt about him.

Her aunt said, "I don't know, I could be wrong in helping you, but I think I know this young man you're in love with. It seems all the pueblos know about him. Anyway, his name is Vicente. He comes from some pueblo up north, I don't know which. I hear he comes from a fine family, and they have many sheep. I heard he was heading south to see some relatives before returning home."

Maria told her mother of the young man she had met. She told her how she had treated him and how much she loved him. Now, she said, she must go and find him, for he was her very life. If anyone tried to stop her she would run off.

So Maria and her younger brother saddled up their horses and set out to find Vicente. They rode downstream, going south along the river. Late that afternoon they came to the first village, the Pueblo of Santo Domingo. There they asked about Vicente. They were told he had been there but had gone on. They rested that night. Early the next morning they set out again.

Before going far, Maria was surprised to find a piece of purple silk cloth hanging on a bush. Maria's brother said, "It looks like he is tearing up his purple shirt into strips to guide us."

Maria became excited, and her heart began to beat faster. Now she felt he loved her too. Perhaps he thought she chased him away because she had already accepted someone else in her own village, so he went on home.

Late that afternoon, when they came to San Felipe Pueblo, they found he had been there but had moved on, this time heading back north. They rested at San Felipe for the night. Early in the morning they headed back north, following the purple strips, until they came back to the Pueblo of Santo Domingo. There they were told he had passed through after a short rest. Again they followed the purple strips, and Maria's heart seemed to be pounding faster. She felt they were catching up to him.

The trail led back to her home pueblo of Cochiti. Here he had rested as if he were waiting for them to catch up. But he had left, and again they followed the strips, which led through San Ildefonso Pueblo and on toward Santa Clara Pueblo.

Maria's heart could not stand the strain. She ate very little and slept less. They had traveled a long way, and by the time they finally reached Santa Clara Pueblo they were very tired and hungry. The people of Santa Clara fed them, gave them a place to rest, and told Maria he had been there the day before. They were sure she would find him in the next village, the Pueblo of San Juan.

Maria was ill with fever, and her health was failing badly. She wanted to go on, but her brother and the people of Santa Clara begged her to remain with them until she was strong enough to travel again. They said their horses were also worn out and needed rest.

The pueblo medicine man came to where she was staying and gave her some mountain tea to drink. He told her it would put her to sleep for a while. She slept for two days.

While she was asleep, a rider from Santa Clara went to San Juan, where he found Vicente and told him of Maria.

After two days of good rest and sleep, Maria woke up. To her surprise Vicente was sitting by her bedside. He reached for her hand. Squeezing it gently he said, "Rest here, Maria, until you are strong again. Then I'll take you to my home in San Juan and we will be married. You have proved your love for me, now I must prove my love for you."

LITTLE SINGER
A Navajo Love Story

Little Singer had been a loner since he was a young boy. He was an orphan who had been adopted and raised by his aunt and uncle. His uncle was a man rich in horses, and his horses were well known far and wide. His aunt was rich in sheep. When Little Singer reached his eighth birthday, his aunt gave him five head of sheep, for that was the Navajo way of bringing a child into the family and making him a part of the settlement. His small flock would start him out in life, but he was expected to earn his flock by herding his aunt's sheep. His uncle gave him four young colts, which he would learn to raise and train, as he herded his uncle's horses.

Now, seventeen years old, Little Singer was on his way to a big sing, a curing sing, all by himself. There he would sell or trade two of his horses. The sing would last seven days. His uncle didn't go with him, because he wanted Little Singer to learn to take care of himself. Little Singer rode his roan stallion and led his other two horses. He was happy, for everything was in beauty *(HOZ ho')*. He knew he could get a good trade or good money for his horses.

He rode his horse as if the two were one creature in motion, all in perfect rhythm. He rode in the style of the northeast clans, leaning back on his haunches, his long legs stretching forward, his red cowhide moccasins pressing lightly in the stirrups. On the back of his head rested his American hat, held in place by a leather chin string, and his long black hair was tied up in the chungo-bun style of his people. The large silver concho belt around his slim waist clanked with every jump his horse took over the bushes in their path. The dry cool air stung his face, making his eyes water and his ears

135

burn, but he rode in beauty. He started singing the song of happiness:

Wherever I go, wherever I go
Wherever I am, there is happiness
To a singing I go, long distance I go
Wherever I go, whatever I see, there is happiness.

He rode over low hills and through small valleys. Toward the end of the day he began to see the camps of his people, and he knew he had arrived at the big sing. He rode by a family who had just settled down from their journey.

The woman had a fire going. On hearing him, she straightened up and said, "Stop and rest, grandfather. I will soon have some coffee ready and later some food."

Little Singer smiled and replied, "It is good, good mother, but I am not yet ready to rest. I am called Little Singer, I am of the Encircled Mountain *(Dsilan-oth-il-ni)* Clan. I have horses to sell or trade."

Little Singer moved on, searching for a good place
to picket his horses for the night. He soon came
upon a low hill with clumps of cedar and juniper
and a small pond of water fed by a stream from a
cedar-covered hill behind him. Other people were
camped close by, but he was able to find a good
spot to make camp and picket his horses. He knew
they would be safe there.

The family next to him invited him to share their
meal of mutton stew and roasted corn. He accepted.
When the sun went down and evening settled over
the area, the bonfires were lit and the drums began
to beat slowly, calling the people to gather around
for the dance. Groups of young men came in
together, some to stand around the singers, others
to watch the girls.

Before too long men began to ride up and form a
semicircle around the edge of the people. Little
Singer guided his horse into the line of riders.
Upright burning logs sent dancing orange tongues
of fire into the cool air, and the popping of

firebrands competed with the singing. Huge night shadows followed the horsemen, whose faces were bright in the firelight, and their horses' eyes glared green and red like the eyes of the monsters of old.

Soon shouts, calls and laughter shifted attention to the crowd as young girls and women pulled partners into the dance. Little Singer saw a pretty girl in blue come into the light from out of nowhere. She edged toward the crowd and grabbed the blanket of a tall man, forcing him to dance with her. He pretended to hold back as if he didn't want to dance, but he was all smiles when the song was over and he paid the girl. The girl quickly disappeared into the crowd.

Little Singer had kept his eyes on the girl as she danced. She was the prettiest girl he had ever seen, and it seemed as if his whole world was changed now that he had seen her. His heart longed for her. He was brought back to the world about him when a young horseman next to him asked, "Who was that pretty girl in blue who grabbed the tall man?"

Little Singer replied, "I don't know, I am not
from here."

"She is pretty—perhaps I will let her catch me,"
the young horseman said and laughed loudly.

Little Singer stood up on his stirrups to get a better
look over the crowd, as he searched for the girl in
blue. Finally he saw her way in the back with three
other girls. They were laughing and pointing at
each other as if they were making fun of each
other. Perhaps they were daring each other to
choose certain partners.

The three girls all wore their long black hair loose,
hanging back on their shoulders Mohave style.
They wore high red-leather moccasins, silver-and-
turquoise concho belts around their waists, and
velveteen blouses and skirts—one wore purple, one
wore green, and the prettiest one wore blue.

The pretty girl suddenly turned toward Little
Singer and the other horsemen, as if she were
looking for someone special. It seemed they were

looking at each other. He felt his heart beating faster, he tried to look away but her eyes had turned him to stone. She was smiling the prettiest smile he had ever seen, prettier than a rainbow. He was sure she was looking at him and not at one of the other horsemen. He had never felt this way before. He had seen other girls in his settlement at the trading post. He had met a girl once who was out herding her sheep and he thought he liked her, but not the way he liked this girl in blue.

When the horse next to him suddenly got restless, he looked away for a short moment. When he turned back, the girl had disappeared from sight. Worried now, he looked and looked for her but did not see her anywhere—not among the dancers, not in the crowd, not with the other two girls. Then the singing started once more with a new group of singers. The women came out again to choose partners.

Little Singer did not see the pretty girl in the dance circle. He thought she must have gone away.

Perhaps she had a boyfriend and had left the dance to meet him. Little Singer was sick in his heart. He didn't care about the dance or the singing, and he thought to himself, Oh, I bet she's no good, I don't care for her, let her go to her boyfriend.

Little Singer felt so angry and hurt that he decided he would leave too. As he was about to back his horse out of the circle, he remembered something his uncle had once said. "When you become angry at someone or something," his uncle told him, "you should sing, that will calm you down."

Little Singer asked the horseman on his right to hold his horse for him while he joined the singing, and the man agreed. Little Singer joined the singers. As he sang he was in his own world, but then he caught sight of the pretty girl pulling a man from the crowd into the dance circle.

He shut his eyes, trying to forget her. Why must she keep on teasing him? He felt sure she was teasing him. Finally he turned his back to the dancers so he wouldn't see her anymore. He sang almost until dawn. He went back for his horse and rode away to his camp. He rolled up in his blanket and lay down on the ground by his neighbor's fire and fell asleep.

Little Singer woke up early the next morning to the sweet aroma of boiling coffee. The woman was also roasting sheep ribs. The aroma of the food reminded his stomach that he hadn't eaten most of yesterday and last night.

After first checking on his horses, he washed his face. He felt someone was watching him. He looked up and saw the pretty girl by a cedar tree. He felt uneasy, why was she there? Did she follow him when he left the dance, was she teasing him?

Just then the woman of the camp called for him, "Come, grandfather, come have some coffee and meat." Little Singer looked quickly toward the woman, and when he turned back to the pretty girl, she was gone. He was puzzled, but he was also very hungry, so he went over to the camp. He sat down on the ground by the campfire, and the woman

handed him a tin cup of hot coffee, some small
round bread, and some sheep ribs.

As he ate, he could think of nothing but the girl.

The woman who had shared her food with him
said, "That girl stood there watching you, maybe
you forgot to pay her when you danced with her."

Little Singer smiled at her teasing. Then he said,
"Little Mother, you are a good cook, like my aunt. I
am of the Encircled Mountain Clan, I am called
Little Singer."

The woman replied, "We are of the Muddy Water
Clan. You are welcome in our camp." After Little
Singer had eaten, he tended his horses. Later that
day he took two horses and went through the
camps telling people he had horses for sale.

Late that afternoon he sold the two horses for
many Mexican silver dollars, which he knew he
could sell or trade to those who made silver jewelry.
He went back to camp and gave the woman two
silver dollars.

That evening he rode back to the dance to the same place as before. He waited there, looking everywhere for the girl, but she was nowhere to be seen.

As the singing started, his heart began to pound. He felt sure she would come out now. He sat up straight in the saddle, stretching his neck, looking for her.

Little Singer felt a tugging on his moccasin. He looked down and saw the pretty girl standing alongside his horse. He gave her a weak smile as she said, "Come, let's dance."

Little Singer blushed. "I can't," he replied. "I don't know how to dance, I have never danced."

The girl was angry. "Perhaps you are too good for me," she said. She pulled on his moccasin and said, "Perhaps you have a girlfriend or even a wife at home. Why do you look at me if you don't want me? Don't look at me anymore!" She turned and quickly slipped away in the darkness.

144

Little Singer wanted to call her back, but she was gone. He wanted to tell her how he felt about her. He wanted to tell her he had never danced in a squaw dance before. He had seen many of them but never danced. He tried to forget what had happened, but he couldn't erase her words and her anger from his mind. He tried to think but he couldn't, she had taken his thinking with her. Darkness had taken him from his world. His thoughts were no longer his own, they belonged to the girl. He had to find her again.

The horseman on his left grinned at him. "What is wrong, uncle?" he teased, "you afraid of girls?"

Little Singer replied, "No, I am not afraid of anything, but who is that girl? Where is she from?"

The horseman replied, "I am not from here, I don't know her or her clan. I hear she is a schoolgirl at the mission of the long brown coats, to the east of here. She is in training to be one of them. They say the mission women do not marry, they leave the world of our people and go into their own world."

The singing had begun again, and women were out looking for partners. He saw the pretty girl go up to a man in a high-crown American hat. As she danced she glanced at Little Singer, teasing him. He thought she wanted to hurt him because, why did he come into her life and then let her down? That must have been what was in her heart.

She finished the dance with her partner and left him without bothering to get paid. As she hurried to her friends, one of them asked, "What's wrong? You're not the same person. Have you fallen in love with one of those wild boys?"

The pretty girl replied, "Oh, it is nothing. I just want to go back, it is no fun here."

Early the next morning the girls left. Little Singer saw them go. His heart was sad and heavy. He felt his love for her growing stronger, but he was puzzled by what the horseman had said of the mission school of the long brown coats. Why did the women never marry?

The big sing went on, but he wasn't interested. He had sold his horses, and he had money. It was time to go home.

When his uncle met Little Singer at the horse corral, he could see the boy was troubled. Little Singer always came home singing at the top of his voice, but this day he came in silence, his head resting on his chest. Perhaps he was sick or had tasted the whiskeys the Mexicans sell or trade among the people.

They talked for a long time. Little Singer told his uncle of the pretty girl and said he wanted to marry her.

His uncle asked, "Where is she from? What is her clan, and what is her name?"

Little Singer replied, "She left before I could find out. The only thing I heard is that she is a schoolgirl at a mission of the long brown coats. I didn't talk to her much but I know I want her for my wife."

His uncle was silent for a long time. Then he said, "If that is the true wish of your heart, it is good. I've heard of this mission place, it's only three days' ride from here."

Little Singer's uncle told him how to get to the school. He warned his nephew that the school and the police would make trouble when he took the girl away.

Early the next morning, Little Singer set out to find the mission and the girl. Late on the third afternoon he rode over a hill and saw a cluster of brown stone buildings in the valley below. He left his horse in a clump of cedar trees and edged closer to the mission. He hid behind a large bush near one of the big square hogans. He saw some young Navajo boys throwing a big round ball at a square board fastened to the top of a long pole.

His heart almost stopped when he saw the pretty girl. She was with the same two girls. They all wore American skirts of the same dark-blue color. He

148

edged closer, keeping his eyes on her. Then she and her friends began to walk in his direction, not knowing he was close by.

She was only a few feet away from him, and he could not keep his heart calm. Forgetting all caution, he softly called, "Pretty girl."

She stopped and looked around. Who could be calling her? No, it could not be, she thought, it could not be the horseman the woman near his camp called "Little Singer." Her heart was pounding. She didn't know what to do.

"Someone out there called for you," one of her friends said. "It's not your wild horseman, is it?"

The pretty girl's breath came short and fast. "What shall I do?" she asked.

Her friend replied, "Perhaps it is wrong for him to come here and worse for you to be seen with him. The sisters are sure to punish you."

Just then one of the men of the long brown coats came by and asked, "What is wrong, my children? You are not doing anything bad or wrong, are you? You are not using tobacco?"

One of the girls replied, "No, Father, we are just taking a walk, we will go back before long."

The girls waited till the father was out of sight. The pretty girl said, "I am going to see Little Singer and talk with him. Will you help me, will you keep watch in case someone comes?"

The girls replied, "We are your best friends, we will help you."

She called for Little Singer. After a little while he edged out from behind a cedar tree.

When the pretty girl came to him, he put his arms around her shoulders. "I looked for you every night at the big sing," he said, "but I couldn't find you. I wanted to tell you I liked you the first time I saw you. I think of you all the time. I don't know how to say what I mean, there are no words to say

150

how good my heart feels when I see you. Now that
you are near me, my heart wants to jump out of
my body.

"I want to take you with me, will you go with me? I
have sheep and horses, and my uncle will help me
build your hogan. I have talked with him. He took
a long time to answer, but when he did, he said it
was good. He also said I might get in trouble with
the school and the Navajo police would come and
get me, but he will help us. He said I was to talk to
your family, but I don't know where you come
from, or your clan, or you name. Only that I call
you pretty girl."

"My name is War in the Sky, but at the mission
they call me Sadie," she replied. "I belong to my
mother's clan, the Sage Brush Hill (Tsayishid-hui)
Clan. My home is north of here, a place called
Chusca (TsusKai-Tso-is-Kai)." She laughed a little
and said, "I was to be one of the mission sisters
who never marry, but now I don't want to stay with
them. I am seventeen years old, I can marry now.

Yes I will go with you."

War in the Sky went back to her friends and told them she wanted to be with Little Singer and she was leaving with him.

Little Singer guided her to his horse and helped her to mount. "We have a long ride, we'll travel by night and hide in the daytime."

"Why can't we both ride?" she asked. "I want to be close to you."

Little Singer replied, "Two of us riding will be heavy on the horse, and the police will be able to follow our trail easier. This way I can erase our trail."

They traveled all night. War in the Sky was asleep part of the time, and Little Singer sang softly to her.

Early the next morning they came to some ruins of the ancient ones. War in the Sky said, "We can hide in there."

Little Singer replied, "No, we would be easy to
find there. I was here once, I know where we can
hide. There's a cave with an opening hidden by
a large bush. I'm sure they don't know about it,
because our people don't even like to come here—
they fear and respect the home of the ancient
ones. We can wait and watch for them from
the cave."

Just then the ancient gods became angry, for some
humans were coming to bother their homes, and
they called on the storm god to erase the trail,
erase the sun, make the earth mother dark, and let
the sand blind their eyes.

Little Singer had just led the horse into the cave
when a fierce sandstorm came roaring through the
canyon, catching the trailing Navajo police out in
the open. They blindly hurried on, trying to keep
their back to the storm. They came by the bush
that hid the cave.

One of the police said, "Let's get behind that bush
and wait out the storm." They stopped right by the

bush, but the stinging sand blurred their vision and made them close their eyes.

Little Singer and War in the Sky held their breath, and their hearts almost stopped. What if the policemen found the cave and came in and caught them? What would he do? Little Singer thought, I'll fight them, I will not let them take Pretty Girl from me.

She held on tightly to Little Singer and whispered, "Don't let them take me back."

Little Singer took out his hunting knife and was ready to fight when one of the policemen said, "Let's go on, we can't stay here, the spirits of the ancient ones are here, and they are angry and will put a curse on us. Let's go back and tell the brown coats we could not find the girl and the boy."

The other policeman said, "That is good. I hope the boy and girl find their way home."

THE LOVE RAINBOW
A Tohono O'Odham (Papago) Story

At one time most parents of the Tohono O'Odham
Nation told their children a traditional love story. It
was a story of a strong love between a young boy
and a young girl.

According to Tohono O'Odham tradition,
becoming a warrior was the first step in becoming
a man. Before a young man could marry, he
needed to prove himself as a warrior. The boy
would be trained in tracking, hunting and the
making of weapons. He would go on raids in
Apache country and even kill an enemy. Then he
would have to go through a ceremony to be
purified. In other cases, a boy would be
apprenticed to a medicine man, and in two to five

years, the apprentice would become a medicine man. And before a couple could marry, the young girl had to reach the age of puberty.

This story begins in an old village called Shahd Kam (Wild Sweet Potatoes). The village was known far and wide for its beautiful maidens. Young men came from the other Tohono O'Odham villages, from the Akimel O'Odham and Yaqui villages, and even from the villages of their ancient enemies, the Apache. Young men came to court these beautiful young maidens, in hopes of winning one of them for a wife, for not only were these young maidens beautiful, they were also good cooks.

In the village of Shahd Kam there were two families living close together as neighbors. One family had a very beautiful daughter whose name was Ah'at (Desert Lily). In the other family there was a fine young boy whose name was Bebthk (Thunder). These two children grew up as playmates and had always loved playing together. When they were ten years old, they still visited each other.

When they reached their twelfth year, they decided they wanted to marry, and they told their parents. Their parents said they were too young and not ready for marriage.

But the boy and girl felt they must be together. Again they insisted they wanted to marry, and again they were told they were too young. Bebthk's parents told him he could not marry because he was not a warrior yet, and Ah'at's parents told her she could not marry until she reached the age of puberty.

But the two young people insisted they would get married, and they threatened to run off to the Akimels. So the parents decided it would be best to separate the young ones to give them the chance to mature. One day Bebthk was taken away to another village far away to the south, where he was to become a medicine man. He would have to train as an apprentice for two years or more, and by then Ah'at would be old enough to marry.

Bebthk was very hurt and sad. He didn't want to leave his beloved Ah'at, and he vowed he would come back and claim her. Before he left, Ah'at gave him the turquoise nugget she wore around her neck. As she gave it to him, she said, "This turquoise is me, wear it always, and when you come back you will give it back to me. This is a token of our love. It is a charm that will keep us together, no matter how far you may go or for how long. But if I should die of a broken heart when you are gone, you must hurry back here to me and open my heart and put our charm in my heart, for there is where it belongs."

Bebthk then let Ah'at know that he could not bear to lose her forever. He gave her some feathers of different colors that he had taken from wild birds, and kept some for himself. He told her that every time it rained, she was to watch for the colors of the feathers in the sky and hold up her feathers. He would hold up his feathers in the direction of her home. When the two sets of feathers came into view, they would form the rainbow, so that everyone living on the earth mother would see and know of their love, and know that someday he would come back to claim Ah'at as his wife.

ABOUT THE AUTHOR
Herman Grey

Herman Grey, an elderly member of the Mohave
tribe, was born in 1919 in Needles, Arizona. He
received his schooling at Indian boarding schools in
California and Arizona, where he made many
friends from many tribes. A retired Marine, he
married a Pima woman from the Salt River
reservation whom he met at boarding school, where
he was a star athlete. She passed away over twenty
years ago. They had eight children, seven of whom
are still alive, and he delights in his many grandchildren and great grandchildren.

Grey has always loved reading and writing about
his tribe and the other tribes he is familiar with.
He noticed that while collections of Indian folktales

are plentiful, compilations of their love stories are
almost nonexistent, so he set out to fill that void.

Drawing from accounts shared with him by
boarding-school classmates of various tribes,
including the Pima, Tohono O'Odham, Apache,
Hopi and Navajo, Grey carefully crafted the tales in
this book from those personal stories.

Herman Grey lives on the Salt River Pima-
Maricopa Indian Reservation in Scottsdale, Arizona.